Published by Patrick Cameron Limited

Dressing Long Hair
BOOK 4

Contents

Dear reader,

As I travel the world training hairdressers in the art of dressing long hair, I am constantly asked how I am able to create more and more unique styles each year. The answer that I find makes the most sense, is that the more that you share your ideas with other people the more room there is for creativity. It is almost as if there is a finite amount of creativity that you can keep in your brain at any one time and only by sharing these ideas can you move on and release space for new inspiration.

Building on the success of my previous videos and books I am delighted to be able to share with you 15 new long hair styles in "Dressing Long Hair Book 4". In this book I am demonstrating some of my latest techniques, which give the styles shape and texture, quickly and easily and will revolutionise the way you work with long hair. "Dressing Long Hair Book 4" will I hope become another hairdressing classic that will help and inspire hairdressers around the world.

Patrick Cameron

Patrick Cameron has justly earned his place in hairdressing's hall of fame as one of the world's leading international hair stylists. Patrick was born in New Zealand but settled in London in 1987 where he recognised a need for further education in dressing long hair.

He perfected a step by step technique that was simple, stylish and easy to understand. Since then Patrick has built a reputation as one of the world's best known hairdressing educators and performers.

Renowned for his immaculate upswept styles, and taking his inspiration from an eclectic variety of sources, year after year he grabs the hairdressing headlines with his imaginative long hair creations. Recently Patrick was honoured by The Guild of Hairdressers with their highest award, recognising Patrick's outstanding commitment and contribution to the hairdressing industry. On receiving his award Patrick commented "I never expect to receive acclamation for something I love doing but when this happens it really does put the icing on the cake as it were."

Elegant Curls

Before/Vorher/Prima/Antes

- Section hair using fingers only (combing or brushing sections would destroy curl definition).
- Haar nur mit den Fingern teilen (Kämmen oder Bürsten der Partien würde die Lockendefinition zerstören).
- Dividere i capelli in sezioni usando solo le dita (pettinando o spazzolando le sezioni si rovinerebbe la definizione dei riccioli).
- Divida el cabello en varias partes utilizando sólo los dedos (si lo hace con un peine o un cepillo, destruirá la definición de los rizos).

- Then back to occipital area in a triangular shape.
- Dann in Dreiecksform zurück zum Hinterkopf.
- Ritornare quindi all'area occipitale in una forma triangolare.
- A continuación, el cabello vuelve a la zona occipital formando un triángulo.

- Section from temple to temple
- Von Schläfe zu Schläfe abteilen.
- Dividere in sezioni da tempia a tempia.
- Divídalo de sien a sien.

- Hold top section forward in a soft twist. Start at right side and use fingers to rake hair back behind ears.
- Oberes Teil in einer sanften Drehung nach vorn halten. Auf der rechten Seite beginnend mit den Fingern das Haar zurück hinter die Ohren kämmen.
- Mantenere in avanti la sezione superiore con un leggero attorcigliamento. Iniziare sul lato destro ed usare le dita per raccogliere nuovamente i capelli dietro le orecchie.
- Sujete la parte superior hacia adelante en una onda suave. Comience por el lado derecho y utilice los dedos para llevar el cabello hacia atrás, detrás de las orejas.

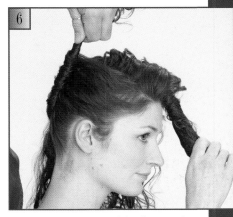

- Twist section toward the face and up to crown.
- Strähne zum Gesicht und hoch zum Scheitel drehen.
- Attorcigliare la sezione verso il viso e fino al cocuzzolo.
- Enrolle el mechón hacia la cara y hacia arriba en dirección a la coronilla.

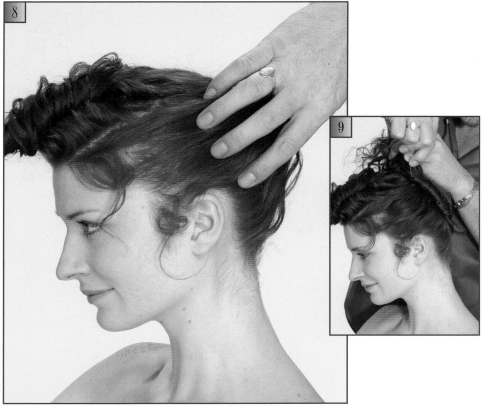

- Clip to hold by running hair grip down the edge of the twist.
- Mit Klemme befestigen, indem man mit der Haarklemme entlang des Abschlusses der verdrehten Strähne nach unten geht.
- Collocare la forcina fermando i capelli lungo l'estremità dell'attorcigliamento.
- Sujételo deslizando una horquilla hacia abajo, hacia el borde de la onda.

- Repeat steps 5,6 & 7 on left side • Schritte 5 bis 7 auf der linken Seite wiederholen
- Ripetere le fasi 5,6 e 7 sul lato sinistro • Repita los pasos 5, 6 y 7 en el lado izquierdo

- Place section clip on tails of twists.
- Strähnenclip an Enden der verdrehten Strähnen anbringen.
- Mantenere la forcina sulle code degli attorcigliamenti.
- Coloque pinzas en los extremos de las ondas.

- Place top section back and between side sections.
- Oberes Teil zurück und zwischen die seitlichen Partien legen.
- Riportare la sezione superiore indietro e tra le sezioni laterali.
- Peine el mechón superior hacia atrás y entre los mechones ondulados.

- Using a large tooth comb softly backcomb to increase volume.
- Mit einem groben Kamm sanft zurückkämmen um mehr Volumen aufzubauen.
- Usando un pettine a denti grossi, cotonare delicatamente per aumentare il volume.
- Con un peine de púas grandes, peine el cabello hacia atrás con suavidad, para aumentar el volumen.

- Push top section forward slightly to create softness and hair grip to hold between twisted sections.
- Oberes Teil leicht nach vorn drücken um Weichheit zu erreichen und mit Haarklemme zwischen den verdrehten Partien befestigen.
- Spingere leggermente in avanti la sezione superiore per creare morbidezza ed una buona presa dei capelli tra le sezioni attorcigliate.
- Empuje el mechón superior un poco hacia adelante para crear una sensación de suavidad y use horquillas como sujeción entre los mechones retorcidos

- Softly backcomb left and right tails.
- Die linken und rechten Strähnen sanft zurückkämmen.
- Cotonare delicatamente le code destre e sinistre.
- Peine hacia atrás los extremos derecho e izquierdo.

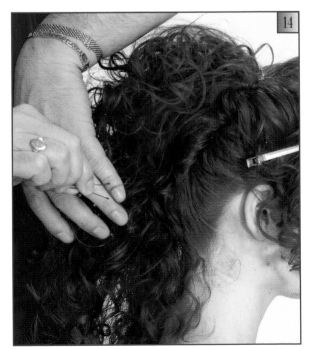

- In between the 2 twists hair grip accordingly to create shape.
- Zwischen die beiden verdrehten Strähnen entsprechend Haarklemme zur Gestaltung der Form stecken.
- Nello spazio tra i 2 attorcigliamenti, fermare i capelli in modo da creare forma.
- Coloque una horquilla entre las dos ondas para dar forma.

17

- Softly cross left tail over right to create height and cover hair grips.
- Linke Strähne sanft über die rechte kreuzen um Höhe zu schaffen und Haarklemmen abzudecken
- Incrociare delicatamente la coda sinistra con la destra in modo da creare altezza e coprire le forcine.
- Cruce con suavidad el extremo de la izquierda sobre el de la derecha, para crear una sensación de altura y para ocultar las horquillas.

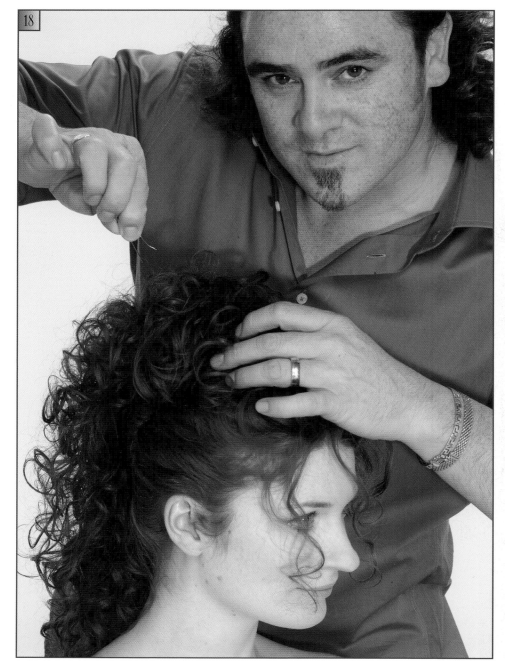

18

- Hair grip into place and check final shape.
- Mit Harrklemme feststecken und endgültige Form überprüfen.
- Collocare la forcina nel punto adatto e verificare la posizione finale.
- Coloque la horquilla en su sitio y revise la forma final.

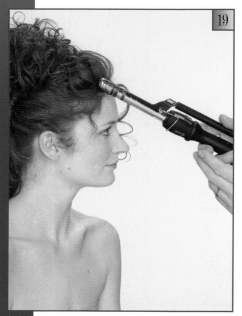

19

- Hot tong for extra curl and softness around face.
- Lockenstab für Extra-Locke und weiche Form rund ums Gesicht
- Applicare il ferro caldo per ottenere un maggiore arricciamento ed una maggiore morbidezza intorno al viso.
- Use unas tenacillas calientes para rizar y suavizar más el cabello alrededor de la cara.

20

- Hair spray to add shine and hold.
- Mit Haarspray für Glanz und Halt schaffen.
- Applicare lo spray sui capelli per ottenere una maggiore brillantezza ed una migliore presa.
- Aplique laca para aportar brillo y fijación al cabello.

Assymetric Chignon

Before/Vorher/Prima/Antes

- Create parting on a diagonal from front left to behind right ear.
- Einen Scheitel in Diagonale von der linken Stirn bis hinter das rechte Ohr ziehen.
- Creare la scriminatura su una linea digonale partendo dalla parte anteriore sinistra per arrivare dietro l'orecchio destro.
- Haga la raya en diagonal. desde la parte delantera izquierda hasta detrás de la oreja derecha.

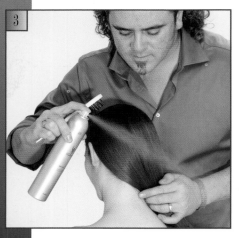

- Place hair from left side into a ponytail on right of neck.
- Das Haar von der linken Seite in einem Pferdeschwanz am rechten Hals zusammenbinden.
- Raccogliere i capelli in una coda di cavallo partendo dal lato sinistro a destra del collo.
- Sujete el cabello de la parte izquierda en una cola a la derecha del cuello.

- Brush left side of hair around to right.
- Linke Seite des Haares zur rechten herum bürsten.
- Spazzolare la parte sinistra dei capelli fino ad arrivare a destra.
- Cepille el cabello de izquierda a derecha

- Right hand side view.
- Ansicht rechte Seite.
- Vista del lato destro.
- Vista del lado derecho

- Smooth right section using soft wax for extra hold and shine.
- Die rechte Partie der Haare glätten, dazu Softwachs für besonderen Halt und Glanz verwenden.
- Appianare la sezione destra usando cera morbida per ottenere una migliore presa ed una maggiore brillantezza.
- Alise la parte derecha del cabello utilizando cera suave, para aportar sujeción y brillo.

- Brush back over ear and twist toward right.
- Über das Ohr zurückbürsten und nach rechts verdrehen.
- Spazzolare all'indietro al di sopra dell'orecchio ed attorcigliare verso destra.
- Cepíllelo hacia atrás por encima de la oreja y ondúlelo hacia la derecha

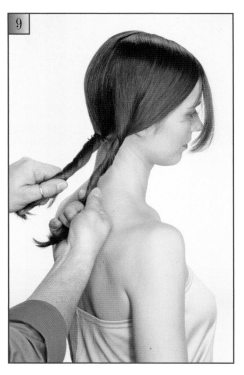

- Twist ponytail toward right (Very important – Both tails twist in the same direction)
- Pferdeschwanz nach rechts verdrehen (sehr wichtig – beide Strähnen drehen in die selbe Richtung)
- Attorcigliare la coda di cavallo verso destra (molto importante: entrambe le code si attorcigliano nella stessa direzione)
- Ondule la cola hacia la derecha (Es muy importante ondular ambas colas en la misma dirección)

- Cross right section over left. • Rechte Partie über die linke kreuzen.
- Far passare la sezione destra al di sopra della sinistra. • Cruce la parte derecha sobre la izquierda.

- Then cross left over right, right over left etc and repeat to end.
- Dann linke über die rechte kreuzen, rechte über linke usw. und bis zum Ende wiederholen.
- Fare quindi passare la sinistra sulla destra, quindi nuovamente la destra sulla sinistra, e così via fino alla fine.
- A continuación, cruce la izquierda sobre la derecha, la derecha de nuevo sobre la izquierda, etc., y siga repitiendo lo mismo hasta terminar.

- Place hair band at end to hold.
- Am Ende mit Haarband befestigen.
- Collocare la fascia di capelli all'estremità per assicurare la presa.
- Sujete el extremo del cabello con una cinta.

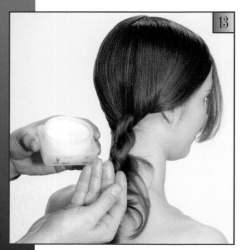

- Use soft wax to separate the strands.
- Softwachs zur Separierung der Strähnen verwenden.
- Usare cera morbida per separare le ciocche.
- Use cera suave para separar los mechones.

- Pull strands of hair out from along the twist.   • Haarfransen aus der Verdrehung zupfen.
- Estrarre ciocche di capelli dall'attorcigliamento.   • Saque algunos mechones de cabello del moño.

- Fold tail back up in a circle towards base.
- Strähne in einem Kreis zurück zum Ansatz falten.
- Ripiegare la coda in un cerchio verso la base.
- Doble la cola hacia la parte superior trasera formando un círculo hacia la base.

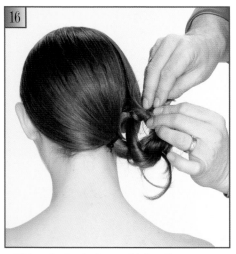

- Hide tail of twist in to middle of base.
- Ende der Flechte in der Mitte des Ansatzes verstecken.
- Nascondere la coda dell'attorcigliamento a metà della base.
- Oculte el extremo de la onda en el centro de la base.

- Hair grip to hold. • Mit Haarklemme befestigen.
- Collocare la forcina per assicurare la presa. • Use una horquilla para sujetar el cabello.

- Smooth front area into a wrap.
- Vorderen Bereich glätten und in einen Umschlag formen.
- Appianare l'area anteriore in un involucro.
- Arregle la parte delantera en una pañoleta.

- Hide tails of wrap into the chignon.
- Strähnen des Umschlags im Chignon verstecken.
- Nascondere le code dell'involucro nello chignon
- Oculte los extremos de la pañoleta dentro del moño.

Trendy Curls

Before/Vorher/Prima/Antes

- Create a rectangular section from temple to temple and back to crown. Place remaining hair into a ponytail on crown.
- Eine rechteckige Partie von Schläfe zu Schläfe und zurück zum Scheitel bilden. Das übrige Haar in einem Pferdeschwanz am Scheitel zusammenbinden.
- Creare una sezione rettangolare da tempia a tempia ed all'indietro fino alla corona. Formare i capelli rimanenti in una coda di cavallo sulla corona.
- Practique una división rectangular de sien a sien, y luego en dirección a la coronilla. Sujete el resto del cabello en una cola en la coronilla.

- Leave pieces out around face and brush remaining hair back.
- Strähnen rund um das Gesicht draußen lassen und übriges Haar zurückbürsten.
- Lasciare dei pezzi intorno al viso e rispazzolare i capelli rimanenti.
- Deje mechones sueltos alrededor de la cara y cepille hacia atrás el resto del cabello.

- Twist hair softly and hair grip into place.
- Haar sanft verdrehen und mit Haarklemme befestigen.
- Attorcigliare delicatamente i capelli e collocare correttamente la forcina.
- Ondule el cabello con suavidad y sujételo con horquillas.

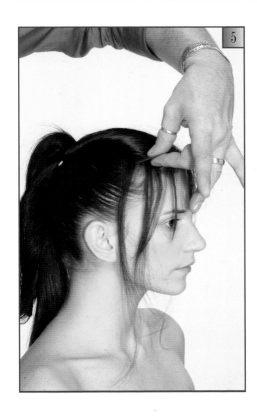

- Pull front of twist gently to create height and softness.
- Vorderseite der Locke sanft herausziehen um Höhe und weiche Form zu schaffen.
- Tirare delicatamente la parte anteriore dell'attorcigliamento per creare altezza e morbidezza.
- Tire un poco de la onda hacia adelante para crear una sensación de altura y suavidad.

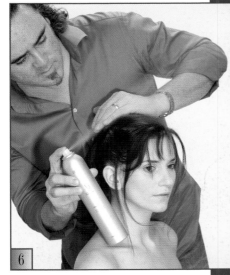

- Hairspray to hold.
- Mit Haarspray Halt geben.
- Applicare lo spray ai capelli per assicurare la presa.
- Aplique laca al cabello para fijarlo

Trendy Curls

15

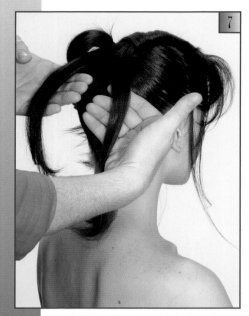

7

- Split tail of front twist into 2 sections.
- Strähne der vorderen Flechte in 2 Partien teilen.
- Dividere la coda dell'attorcigliamento anteriore in 2 sezioni.
- Divida el extremo de la onda delantera en dos partes.Clip to hold by running hair grip down the edge of the twist.

8

- Create a **loose** 2 strand braid by taking a small section from the left side and placing it into the right side.
- Eine **lose** Haarflechte aus 2 Strähnen machen, indem eine kleine Partie von der linken Seite genommen und in die rechte Seite eingefügt wird.
- Creare una treccia **sciolta** a 2 ciocche prelevando una piccola sezione dal lato sinistro e collocandola nel lato destro.
- Haga una trenza **poco apretada** de 2 mechones, utilizando un poco de cabello del lado izquierdo y colocándolo en el lado derecho.

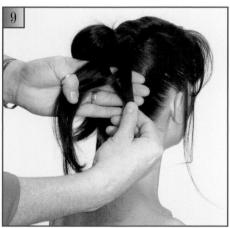

9

- Repeat process by taking a small section from the right side and crossing it over and into the left side.
- Vorgang wiederholen, indem eine kleine Partie von der rechten Seite genommen, überkreuzt und in die linke Seite eingefügt wird.
- Ripetere il procedimento prelevando una piccola sezione dal lato destro e facendola passare al di sopra e all'interno del lato sinistro.
- Repita la misma operación, esta vez trenzando un poco de cabello del lado derecho con el del lado izquierdo.

10

- Repeat until end.
- Bis zum Ende wiederholen.
- Ripetere fino alla fine.
- Repita hasta terminar.

11

- Place band on end of braid.
- Band am Zopfende anbringen.
- Collocare la fascia all'estremità della treccia.
- Coloque una cinta en el extremo de la trenza.

- Divide ponytail into 3 sections and repeat 2 strand braid on each section.
- Pferdeschwanz in 3 Partien teilen und mit jeder Partie wieder einen Zopf aus zwei Strähnen fertigen.
- Dividere la coda di cavallo in 3 sezioni e ripetere la treccia a 2 ciocche su ogni sezione.
- Divida la cola en 3 partes y haga con cada una de ellas trenzas de 2 mechones.

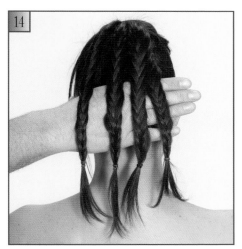

- Finished view of all 4 braids.
- Fertige Ansicht aller vier Zöpfe.
- Vista dell'aspetto definitivo di tutte le 4 trecce.
- Aspecto final de las 4 trenzas.

- Hair grip at base.
- Mit Haarklemme am Ansatz befestigen.
- Collocare la forcina alla base.
- Sujétela en la base con una horquilla.

- Take a very very fine strand of hair from tail of braid. Hold strand firmly, place finger and thumb onto elastic and push braid towards the head.
- Eine sehr, sehr feine Haarsträhne aus der Strähne des Zopfes nehmen. Strähne fest halten, Finger und Daumen um Gummiband halten und Zopf zum Kopf hin drücken.
- Prelevare una ciocca di capelli finissima dalla coda della treccia. Mantenere saldamente ferma la ciocca, collocare il dito ed il pollice sull'elastico e spingere la treccia verso la testa.
- Extraiga un mechón muy fino de cabello del extremo de la trenza. Sujételo fuerte, coloque el índice y el pulgar en una gomila y empuje la trenza hacia la cabeza

- Repeat process until all 4 braids are placed.
- Vorgang wiederholen bis alle 4 Zöpfe befestigt sind.
- Ripetere il procedimento fino a collocare tutte e 4 le trecce.
- Repita la misma operación hasta sujetar las 4 trenzas.

- Back view of placed braids.
- Rückwärtige Ansicht der angebrachten Zöpfe.
- Vista posteriore delle trecce collocate.
- Vista posterior de las trenzas.

- Pull gently at braids to create soft loops and curls.
- Leicht an den Zöpfen zupfen um sanfte Schleifen und Locken zu erzielen.
- Tirare con delicatezza le trecce in modo da creare curve e riccioli morbidi.
- Tire un poco de las trenzas para crear suaves bucles y rizos.

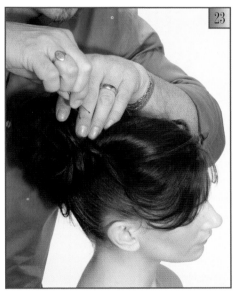

- Style front as desired. • Vorderseite wie gewünscht frisieren.
- Conferire alla parte anteriore lo stile desiderato. • Peine la parte delantera como desee.

- Hairspray to finish for shine and hold.
- Haarspray zum Abschluss für Glanz und Halt.
- Applicare lo spray di rifinitura per ottenere brillantezza e presa.
- Aplique laca para aportar brillo y fijación al cabello.

Twisted Chic

Before/Vorher/Prima/Antes

- Sections from ear to crown to ear, creating front and back.
- Partien von einem Ohr über den Scheitel zum anderen Ohr, damit Vorder- und Hinterseite abtrennen.
- Sezioni da orecchio a corona e da corona ad orecchio, che creano un'area anteriore e una posteriore.
- Practique una división oreja-coronilla-oreja, para crear una parte delantera y otra trasera.

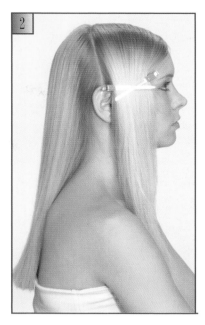

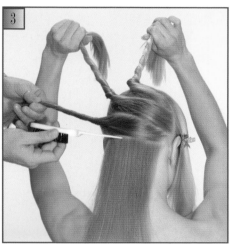

- Divide back area into 4 even, horizontal sections.
- Hinteren Bereich in vier gleich große, waagerechte Partien aufteilen.
- Dividere l'area posteriore in 4 identiche sezioni orizzontali.
- Divida la parte trasera en 4 partes horizontales y similares.

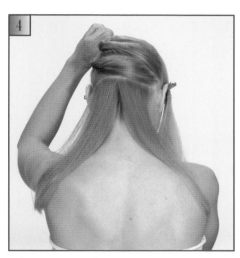

- Starting on our first section at the neck – divide in two.
- Mit der ersten Partie am Hals beginnen, diese in zwei Teile teilen.
- Iniziando dalla nostra prima sezione sul collo – dividere in due.
- Comience por la primera parte de la nuca, dividiéndola en dos.

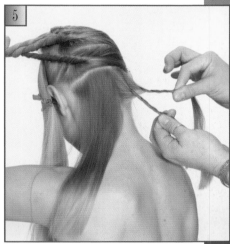

- Cross twists left over right.
- Die verdrehten Strähnen von links nach rechts überkreuzen.
- Incrociare gli attorcigliamenti con il sinistro sopra il destro.
- Cruce la onda izquierda sobre la derecha.

- Split right section into two again and twist both pieces in the same direction towards the left.
- Rechtes Teil nochmals in zwei Teile teilen und beide in derselben Richtung nach links verdrehen.
- Dividere nuovamente in due la sezione destra ed attorcigliare entrambi i pezzi nella stessa direzione verso sinistra.
- Divida la parte derecha también en dos y ondule ambas partes en la misma dirección, hacia la izquierda.

- Then continuing to twist cross right over left.
- Danach weiter rechts und links überkreuz verdrehen.
- Continuare con l'attorcigliamento destro sopra il sinistro.
- A continuación, cruce la onda derecha sobre la izquierda.

8

- Continuing to twist, cross left over right etc until the end thereby creating a rope effect.
- Weiter verdrehen, bis zum Ende links über rechts kreuzen usw. damit einen Seileffekt schaffen.
- Continuare con l'incrocio alternato degli attorcigliamenti fino alla fine, creando un effetto corda.
- Siga ondulando el cabello, cruzando el de la izquierda sobre el de la derecha, etc. hasta terminar, de forma que se crea un efecto como de trenzado.

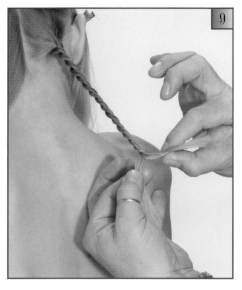

9

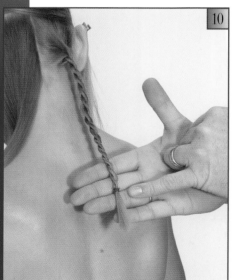

10

- Place band on end.
- Am Ende mit Haargummi fixieren.
- Collocare la fascia sull'estremità.
- Coloque una cinta en el extremo.

11

- Repeat on left section.
- Mit linker Partie wiederholen.
- Ripetere l'operazione sulla sezione sinistra.
- Repita la operación en el lado izquierdo.

- Divide second level into 4 even sections.
- Die zweite Ebene in vier gleiche Partien aufteilen.
- Dividere il secondo livello in 4 sezioni identiche.
- Divida el segundo nivel en 4 partes similares.

12

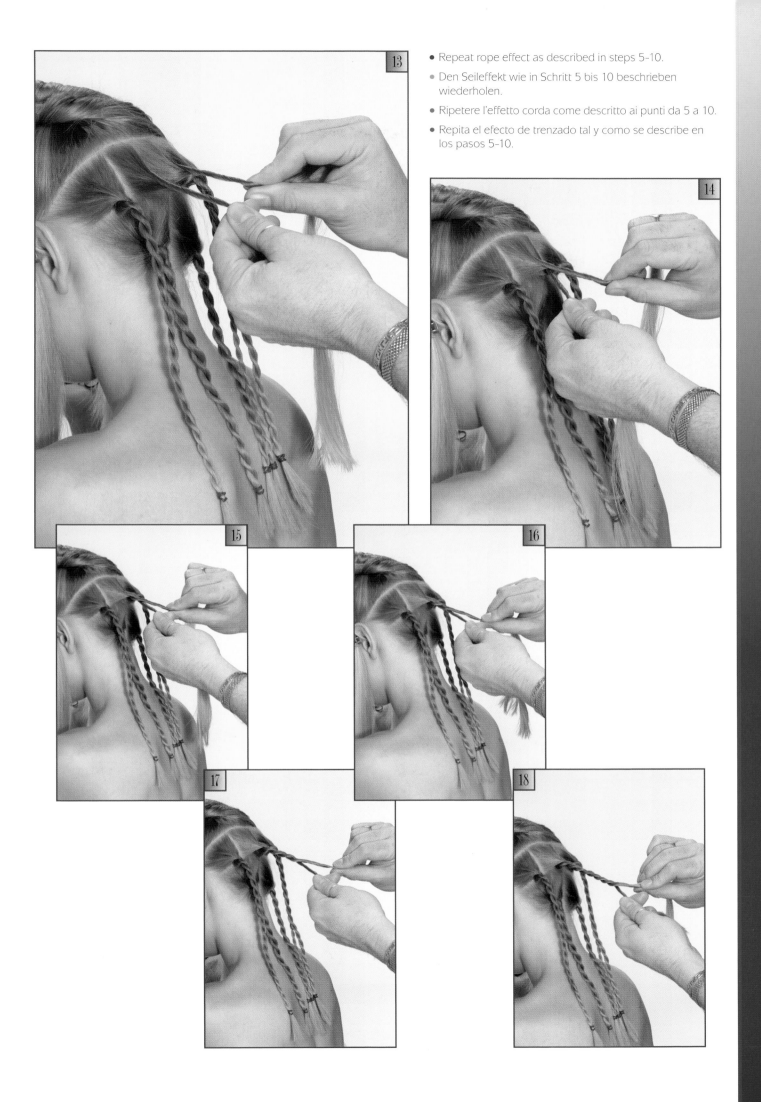

- Repeat rope effect as described in steps 5-10.

- Den Seileffekt wie in Schritt 5 bis 10 beschrieben wiederholen.

- Ripetere l'effetto corda come descritto ai punti da 5 a 10.

- Repita el efecto de trenzado tal y como se describe en los pasos 5-10.

19

- Four completed ropes.
- Vier fertige Seile.
- Quattro corde complete.
- Cuatro trenzados completos.

20

- Divide third level into 4 even sections.
- Die dritte Ebene in vier gleiche Partien aufteilen.
- Dividere il terzo livello in 4 sezioni identiche.
- Divida el tercer nivel en 4 partes similares.

21

- Completed third level.
- Fertige dritte Ebene.
- Terzo livello completato.
- Tercer nivel terminado.

22

- Divide fourth level into 4 even sections.
- Die vierte Ebene in vier gleiche Partien aufteilen.
- Dividere il quarto livello in 4 sezioni identiche.
- Divida el cuarto nivel en 4 partes similares.

23

- Completed fourth level.
- Fertige vierte Ebene.
- Quarto livello completato.
- Cuarto nivel terminado.

24

- Divide front area into 6 even sections and hold with section clips and rope as previously.
- Den vorderen Bereich in 6 gleich große Partien aufteilen und mit Clips befestigen, dann wie vorher seilartig verdrehen.
- Dividere l'area anteriore in 6 sezioni identiche e fermare con forcine di sezione e corda come in precedenza.
- Divida la parte delantera en 6 partes similares, sujételas con pinzas y tréncelas como se explicó antes.

- Completed front area.
- Fertiger vorderer Bereich.
- Area anteriore completa.
- Parte delantera terminada.

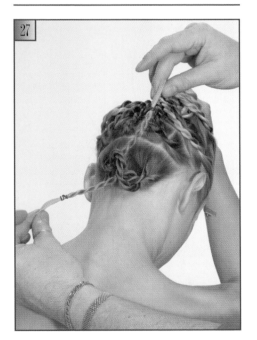

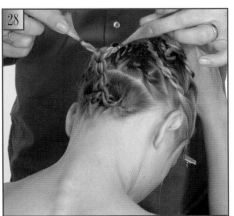

- Starting at our first level at the neck, tie the 2 ropes into several loose knots, one after the other.
- Beginnend mit unserer ersten Ebene am Hals je zwei Seile nacheinander in mehreren losen Knoten verknoten.
- Iniziando dal nostro primo livello sul collo, legare le 2 corde in diversi nodi sciolti.
- Comenzando por el primer nivel de la nuca, ate las 2 trenzas en varios nudos sueltos, uno después del otro.

- Hide tails under and hair grip into place.
- Strähnen untendrunter verstecken und mit Haarklemmen befestigen.
- Nascondere le code al di sotto e collocare in posizione la forcina.
- Oculte los extremos por debajo y sujételos con horquillas.

- Take right tail of middle rope and tie into a knot with the right side rope.
- Rechts Strähne des mittleren Seils nehmen und in einem Knoten mit dem rechten Seil verknoten.
- Prelevare la coda destra della corda centrale e legare in un noto con la corda posta sul lato destro.
- Ate el extremo derecho de la trenza central en un nudo con la trenza del lado derecho.

- Completed first and second level.
- Fertige erste und zweite Ebene.
- Primo e secondo livello completati.
- Primer y segundo nivel terminados.

- Take left tail of middle rope and tie into a knot with the left side rope. Repeat 32 & 33 until done.
- Linke Strähne des mittleren Seils nehmen und in einem Knoten mit dem linken Seil verknoten. Schritte 32 und 33 bis zur Fertigstellung wiederholen.
- Prelevare la coda sinistra della corda centrale e legare in un noto con la corda posta sul lato sinistro. Ripetere le operazioni di cui ai punti 32 e 33 fino ad ottenere il risultato.
- Ate el extremo izquierdo de la trenza central en un nudo con la trenza del lado izquierdo. Repita los pasos 32 y 33 hasta terminar.

- Tie middle two ropes in a single knot.
- Die mittleren beiden Seile in einem einzigen Knoten zusammenbinden.
- Legare le due corde centrali in un singolo nodo.
- Ate en el centro dos trenzas en un sólo nudo.

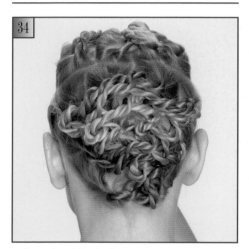

- Completed back view.
- Fertige Hinteransicht.
- Vista posteriore completa.
- Vista posterior terminada.

- Now complete roping and knotting of the 6 front sections as before and place over to join the finished back section.
- Nun das Verdrehen und Verknoten der 6 Partien auf der Vorderseite wie oben fertig stellen, darüber legen und mit der fertigen Hinterpartie vereinigen.
- Completare ora la legatura con corde e l'annodamento delle 6 sezioni anteriori come fatto in precedenza e collocare al di sopra per unire la sezione posteriore completata.
- Ahora, termine de trenzar y anudar las 6 partes delanteras como se ha descrito, y colóquelas encima para unirlas a la parte trasera ya terminada.

Casual Chignon

Before/Vorher/Prima/Antes

- Create a rectangular section from temple to temple and back to crown.
- Eine rechteckige Partie von Schläfe zu Schläfe und zurück zum Scheitel bilden.
- Creare una sezione rettangolare da tempia a tempia ed all'indietro verso corona.
- Practique una división rectangular de sien a sien, y en dirección hacia la coronilla.

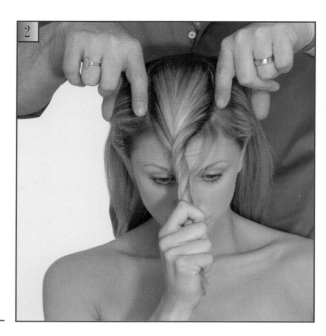

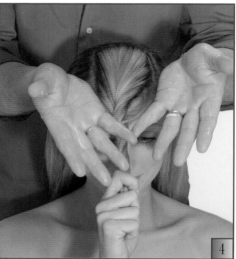

- Apply polish cream to hands and distribute evenly on hands.
- Polish Cream auf Hände aufbringen und gleichmäßig an den Händen verteilen.
- Applicare la crema lucidante alle mani distribuendola in modo uniforme.
- Aplíquese crema de brillo en las manos y repártala de forma uniforme.

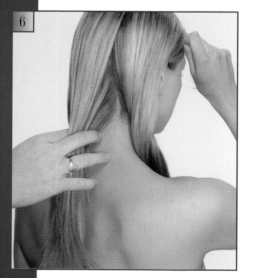

- Divide back area into 3 sections.
- Hinteren Bereich in 3 Partien aufteilen.
- Dividere l'area posteriore in 3 sezioni.
- Divida la zona posterior en 3 partes.

- Run hands through hair to give shine and extra hold.
- Mit Händen durchs Haar fahren, bringt Glanz und extra Halt
- Far passare le mani attraverso i capelli in modo da conferire brillantezza e maggiore presa.
- Deslice las manos por todo el cabello para aportarle brillo y fijación adicionales.

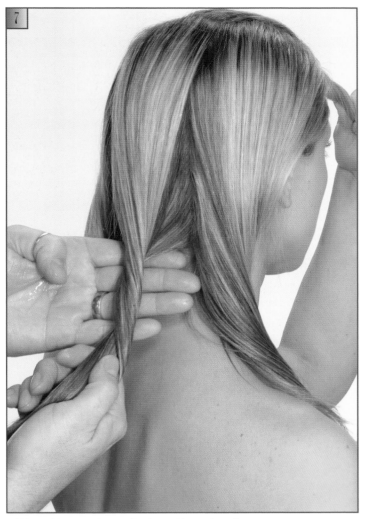

- Take middle section and twist softly to the tail.
- Die mittlere Partie nehmen und sanft bis zum Schwanz verdrehen.
- Prelevare la sezione centrale ed attorcigliare delicatamente fino alla coda.
- Ondule la parte central con suavidad hacia el extremo.

- Pull at the twist to create soft texture.
- An der Locke zupfen um ihre eine weiche Textur zu geben.
- Tirare l'attorcigliamento per creare una consistenza morbida.
- Tire de la onda para crear una textura suave.

- Wrap twist around finger to create a low chignon and hair grip to hold.
- Locke um Finger wickeln und einen niedrigen Chignon herstellen, mit Haarklemme befestigen.
- Avvolgere l'attorcigliamento intorno al dito in modo da creare uno chignon basso ed applicare la forcina per assicurare la presa.
- Envuelva la onda alrededor del dedo para crear un moño bajo y sujételo con horquillas.

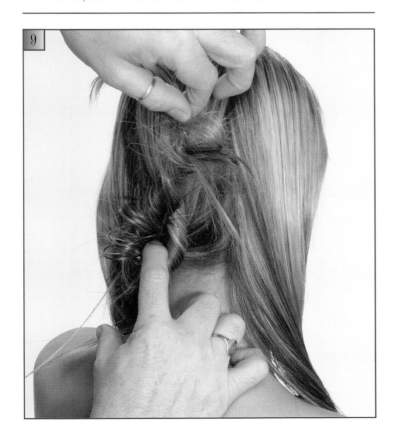

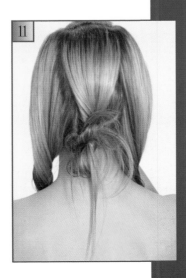

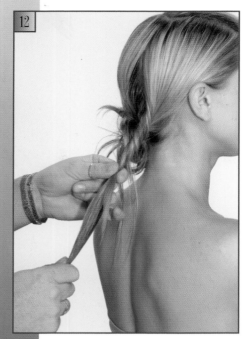

- Pull side section back and twist out from neck to tail.
- Seitliche Partie nach hinten ziehen und vom Hals bis zum Schwanz verdrehen.
- Tirare indietro la sezione laterale ed estrarre attorcigliando dal collo alla coda.
- Tire de la parte lateral hacia atrás y desenróllela empezando por el cuello.

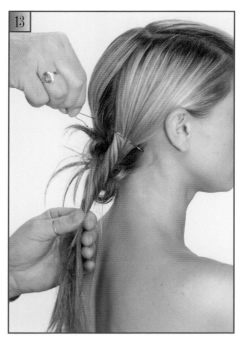

- Hair grip firmly behind ear to hold in place.
- Haarklemme zur Befestigung fest hinters Ohr klemmen.
- Collocare la forcina saldamente dietro l'orecchio in modo da assicurare la presa.
- Sujétela con fuerza con horquillas detrás de la oreja.

- Pull at the twist to create soft texture.
- An der Locke zupfen um ihre eine weiche Textur zu geben.
- Tirare l'attorcigliamento per creare una consistenza morbida.
- Tire de la onda para crear una textura suave.

- Take twist up and over to hide hair grips.
- Locke zum Verdecken der Haarklemme nach oben und darüber ziehen.
- Sollevare l'attorcigliamento per nascondere le forcine.
- Mueva la onda hacia arriba hasta ocultar las horquillas.

- Hair grip into place.
- Haarklemme befestigen.
- Collocare correttamente la forcina.
- Sujete el cabello con horquillas en su sitio.

- Repeat steps 12-16 on opposite side.
- Schritte 12 bis 16 auf der anderen Seite wiederholen.
- Ripetere le fasi da 12 a 16 sul lato opposto.
- Repita los pasos 12-16 en orden inverso.

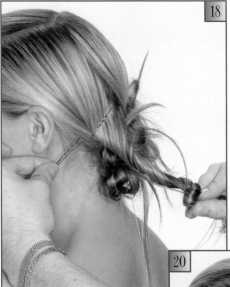

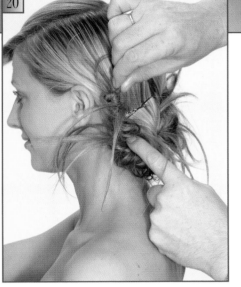

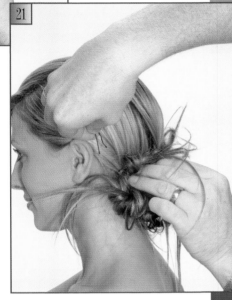

- View of finished back section.
- Ansicht der fertigen hinteren Partie.
- Vista della sezione posteriore completa.
- Vista de la parte posterior acabada.

- Massage polish cream through front section.
- Mit Polish Cream durch die vordere Partie massieren.
- Massaggiare con crema lucidante su tutta la sezione anteriore.
- Aplique con un masaje la crema de brillo por toda la parte delantera.

- Twist top section softly over back of head.
- Obere Partie sanft über dem Hinterkopf verdrehen.
- Attorcigliare delicatamente la sezione superiore al di sopra della parte posteriore della testa.
- Ondule con suavidad la parte delantera hacia la parte posterior de la cabeza.

- Hair grip tail of top twist into chignon.
- Mit Haarklemme Strähne der obersten Locke in Chignon befestigen
- Collocare la forcina sulla coda dell'attorcigliamento superiore all'interno dello chignon.
- Sujete con horquillas el extremo de la onda superior dentro del moño.

- Pull at the twist to create soft texture.
- An der Locke zupfen um ihre eine weiche Textur zu geben.
- Tirare l'attorcigliamento per creare una consistenza morbida.
- Tire de la onda para crear una textura suave.

Simple Elegance

Before/Vorher/Prima/Antes

- Section ear to crown to ear and place back section into a ponytail below crown and off centre.
- Von einem Ohr über den Scheitel bis zum anderen Ohr abteilen und hintere Partie unter dem Scheitel und seitwärts in einem Pferdeschwanz zusammenbinden.
- Sezionare dall'orecchio alla corone e dalla corona all'orecchio e raccogliere la sezione posteriore in una coda di cavallo sotto la corona e fuori dal centro.
- Practique una división oreja-coronilla-oreja y haga una cola con la parte posterior, en la parte central debajo de la coronilla.

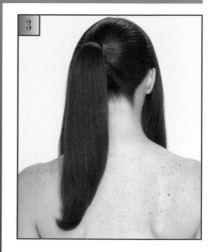

- Place a second hair band half way down the ponytail.
- Einen zweiten Haargummi in der Hälfte des Pferdeschwanzes einbinden.
- Collocare una seconda fascia di capelli a metà della coda di cavallo.
- Coloque una segunda cinta para el cabello en la mitad inferior de la cola.

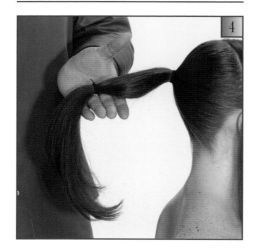

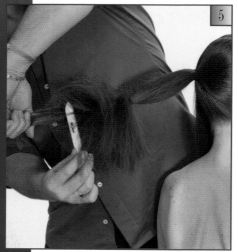

- Backcomb tail into a ball which will provide padding for vertical roll.
- Schwanz in einen Ball zurückkämmen und damit ein Polster für die senkrechte Rolle formen.
- Cotonare la coda in una palla che fornirà l'imbottitura per l'arrotolamento verticale.
- Peine la cola hacia atrás hasta formar un ovillo, que servirá de relleno para la onda vertical.

- Roll backcombed ball to opposite side of base.
- Zurückgekämmten Ball zur gegenüberliegenden Seite des Ansatzes rollen.
- Rotolare la palla cotonata fino al lato opposto della base.
- Enrolle el ovillo hacia el lado opuesto de la base.

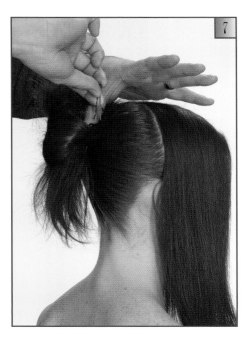

7
- Hair grip second elastic onto scalp.
- Mit Haarklemme das zweite Haargummi am Kopf befestigen.
- Collocare la forcina sul secondo elastico fino al cuoio capelluto.
- Sujete con una horquilla la segunda gomilla.

- Pull hair over and under ball to create semi-circular vertical roll.
- Haar über und unter den Ball ziehen, um eine halbrunde senkrechte Rolle herzustellen.
- Tirare i capelli al di sopra e al di sotto della sfera per creare un rotolo verticale semicircolare.
- Tire del cabello por encima y por debajo del ovillo para crear un rollo vertical semicircular.

8

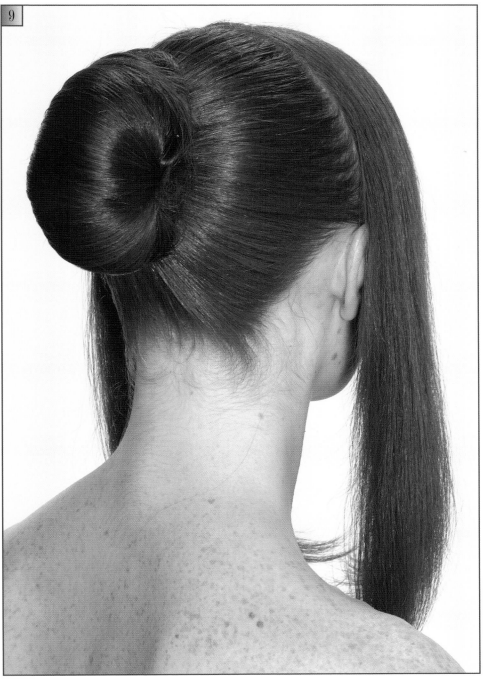

9

10

- Divide front area into 3 sections.
- Vorderen Abschnitt in 3 Partien aufteilen.
- Dividere l'area anteriore in 3 sezioni.
- Divida la zona delantera en 3 partes.

35

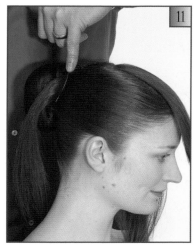

- Brush side section directly back creating width and hair grip tightly to side of roll.

- Seitliche Partie direkt zurückbürsten und damit Breite schaffen, mit Haarklemme fest an Seite der Rolle befestigen.

- Spazzolare la sezione laterale direttamente all'indietro creando una larghezza sufficiente e collocare saldamente la forcina di fianco al rotolo.

- Cepille la parte lateral hacia atrás para crear una sensación de anchura, y sujete el cabello con fuerza con una horquilla en un lado del rollo.

- Repeat on opposite side.

- Auf gegenüberliegender Seite wiederholen.

- Ripetere l'operazione sul lato opposto.

- Repita la operación en el lado contrario.

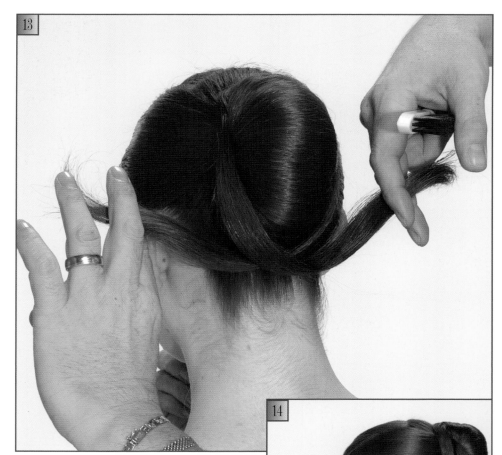

- Cross tails under roll gently and hair grip ends on top of roll.

- Die Strähnen sanft unter der Rolle überkreuzen und Enden mit Haarklemme am oberen Ende der Rolle befestigen.

- Incrociare le code delicatamente sotto il rotolo e collocare la forcina sulle estremità in cima al rotolo.

- Cruce las coletas debajo del rollo con suavidad y sujete con horquillas los extremos en lo alto del rollo.

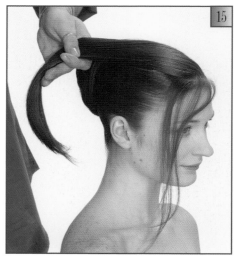

- Brush top area back to one side.

- Oberen Bereich zurück zu einer Seite kämmen.

- Spazzolare all'indietro l'area superiore verso un lato.

- Cepille la parte de arriba hacia un lado.

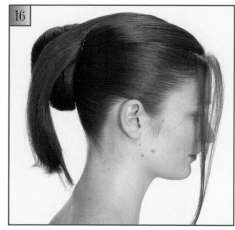

- Place hair grip up and half way through section.

- Haarklemme aufwärts und halb durch die Partie stecken.

- Collocare la forcina in alto e a metà della sezione.

- Coloque horquillas para sujetar el cabello en la parte superior y central.

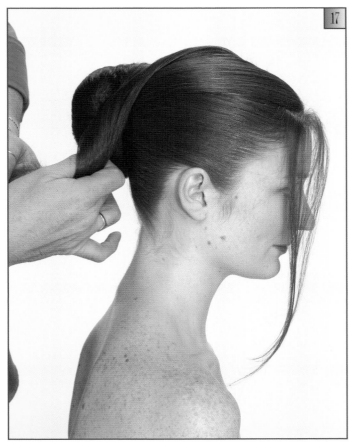

- Twist tail forward to cover hair grip.
- Strähne nach vorn verdrehen, um Haarklemme zu verdecken.
- Attorcigliare la coda in avanti per coprire la forcina.
- Enrolle la coleta hacia adelante para tapar las horquillas.

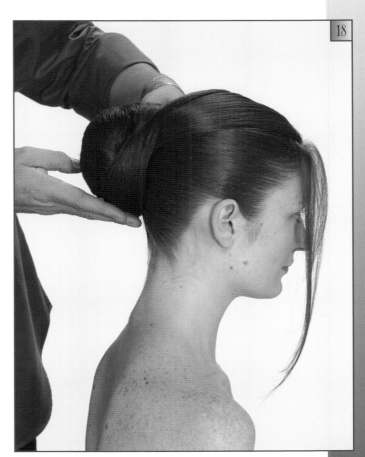

- Gently wrap tail around and under roll.
- Strähne vorsichtig um und unter die Rolle wickeln.
- Avvolgere con delicatezza la coda intorno al rotolo e sotto di esso.
- Envuelva con cuidado la coleta alrededor y por debajo del rollo.

- Place ends under roll on opposite side and hair grip to hold.
- Enden unter der Rolle auf gegenüberliegende Seite legen und mit Haarklemmen befestigen.
- Collocare le estremità sotto il rotolo sul lato opposto e collocare la forcina per assicurare la presa.
- Coloque los extremos debajo del rollo en el lado contrario, y sujételos con horquillas.

- Hair spray for shine and hold.
- Haarspray für Glanz und Halt.
- Applicare lo spray sui capelli per conferire loro brillantezza e presa.
- Aplique laca para aportar brillo y fijación al cabello.

Soft Braids

Before/Vorher/Prima/Antes

- Section hair from temple to temple with fingers and make a loose 3 strand scalp braid back to the crown.

- Haar von Schläfe zu Schläfe mit den Fingern teilen und Bauernzopf aus 3 losen Strähnen zurück zum Scheitel flechten.

- Sezionare i capelli da tempia a tempia con le dita e creare una treccia sciolta di cuoio capelluto a 3 ciocche in posizione posteriore verso la corona.

- Divida el cabello de sien a sien con los dedos y haga una trenza poco apretada de 3 mechones en dirección a la coronilla.

- Finish scalp braid at crown and softly plait tail.

- Bauernzopf am Scheitel beenden und das Strähne locker flechten.

- Completare la treccia di cuoio capelluto sulla corona ed intrecciare la coda con delicatezza.

- Acabe la trenza de espiga en la coronilla y trence con cuidado el extremo.

- As you braid lift hair 1 cm off scalp to create looseness.

- Während des Flechtens das Haar 1 cm von der Kopfhaut anheben, um Lockerheit zu erreichen.

- Mentre vengono formate le trecce, sollevare i capelli di 1 cm. al di fuori del cuoio capelluto per creare scioltezza.

- A medida que vaya trenzando, levante el cabello 1 cm por encima del cuero cabelludo, para que quede la trenza poco apretada.

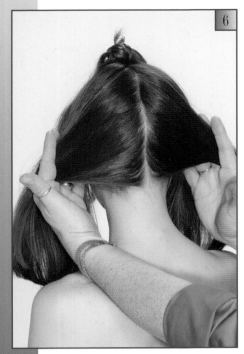

- Section from crown to neck.
- Vom Scheitel zum Hals abteilen.
- Sezionare dalla corona al collo.
- Divida el cabello desde la coronilla al cuello.

- Each side will be divided into 3 sections. Loosely scalp braid first section in a diagonal direction back to parting.
- Jede Seite wird in drei Partien aufgeteilt. Mit der ersten Partie einen lockeren Bauernzopf diagonal zurück vom Scheitel flechten.
- Ogni lato sarà diviso in 3 sezioni. Formare una treccia sciolta sul cuoio capelluto della prima sezione in direzione diagonaled all'indietro verso il punto di separazione.
- Cada lado se dividirá en 3 secciones. Haga una trenza de espiga con la primera parte en dirección diagonal hacia la raya

- Repeat on second section.
- Mit zweiter Partie wiederholen.
- Ripetere l'operazione sulla seconda sezione.
- Repita la operación con la segunda sección de cabello.

- Repeat on third section.
- Mit dritter Partie wiederholen.
- Ripetere l'operazione sulla terza sezione.
- Repita con la tercera sección.

- Repeat steps 7-10 on opposite side.
- Schritte 7 bis 10 auf der anderen Seite wiederholen.
- Ripetere le fasi da 7 a 10 sul lato opposto.
- Repita los pasos 7-10 en el lado contrario.

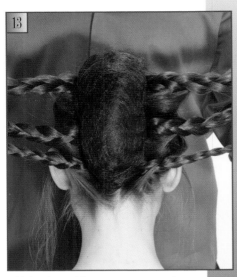

- Hair grip padding over centre parting.
- Polster mit Haarklemmen über Mittelscheitel festklemmen.
- Collocare la forcina sull'imbottitura al di sopra del punto di separazione centrale.
- Sujete con horquillas una almohadilla sobre la raya en medio.

- Take Patrick Cameron hair padding to match colour (see page 89).
- Patrick Cameron Haarpolster in passender Farbe nehmen (siehe Seite 89).
- Prelevare l'imbottitura per capelli Patrick Cameron per far combaciare il colore (vedere alla pagina 89).
- Utilice un relleno de la marca Patrick Cameron adecuado para su color (véase la página 89).

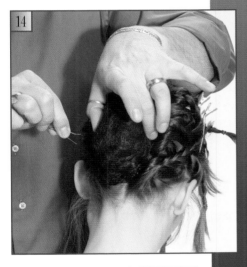

- Starting at the neck pull softly at braid to create loops and texture.
- Am Hals beginnend sanft am Zopf zupfen um Schleifen und Textur zu erzeugen.
- Iniziando dal collo, tirare delicatamente la treccia per creare curve e morbidezza.
- Empezando por el cuello, tire un poco de la trenza para crear bucles y textura.

- Place braid flat onto padding in an S-shape and secure with closed hairgrips though the braid and into padding.
- Zopf flach in S-Form auf Polster legen und mit geschlossenen Haarklemmen durch den Zopf im Polster befestigen.
- Collocare la treccia direttamente sull'imbottitura a forma si S e fermare con forcine chiuse attraverso la treccia e all'interno dell'imbottitura.
- Coloque la trenza plana sobre el relleno en forma de S y sujétela con horquillas cerradas.

- Repeat steps 15-16 on each braid alternating from side to side, covering all the padding.
- Schritte 15 und 16 an jedem Zopf wiederholen, dabei von Seite zu Seite wechseln und somit das ganze Polster abdecken.
- Ripetere le fasi 15 e 16 su ogni treccia alternando i lati e coprendo l'intera imbottitura.
- Repita los pasos 15-16 en cada trenza, alternando entre un lado y otro, hasta cubrir todo el relleno.

- Repeat process on top centre braid and place to finish.
- Verfahren am oberen Mittelzopf wiederholen und diesen endgültig ablegen.
- Ripetere l'operazione sulla treccia centrale superiore e collocare per completare.
- Repita la operación en la trenza de la parte superior central.

Classic Bouffante

Classic Bouffante

Before/Vorher/Prima/Antes

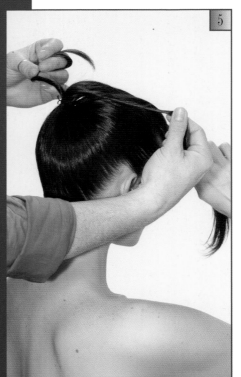

- Create a rectangular section from temple to temple and back to crown. Place remaining hair into a ponytail on crown.

- Eine rechteckige Partie von Schläfe zu Schläfe und zurück zum Scheitel bilden. Das übrige Haar in einem Pferdeschwanz am Scheitel zusammenbinden.

- Creare una sezione rettangolare da tempia a tempia ed all'indietro verso la corona. Raccogliere i capelli rimanenti in una coda di cavallo sulla corona stessa.

- Haga una división rectangular de sien a sien, y hacia atrás en dirección a la coronilla. Haga una cola en la coronilla con el resto del cabello.

- Take a quarter of the ponytail from underneath.

- Ein Viertel des Pferdeschwanzes von unten entnehmen.

- Prelevare un quarto della coda di cavallo dal di sotto.

- Extraiga una cuarta parte de la cola de la parte inferior.

- Divide this quarter section in two and hold with section clips on either side of ear. (These sections will be used in step 22)

- Dieses Viertel in zwei Strähnen teilen und mit Strähnenclips an jeder Seite des Ohres befestigen. (Diese Partien werden in Schritt 22 verwendet)

- Dividere tale quarto di sezione in due e fermare con forcine di sezione su entrambi i lati dell'orecchio (Tali sezioni saranno utilizzate nella fase 22).

- Divida esta parte de cabello en dos, y sujételas con pinzas a cada lado de la oreja. (Estas partes se usarán en el paso 22).

- Take a Patrick Cameron hair padding to match colour. (See page 89)

- Ein Patrick Cameron Harrpolster in passender Farbe nehmen. (Siehe Seite 89)

- Prelevare un'imbottitura di capelli Patrick Cameron per far combaciare il colore (vedere alla pagina 89).

- Utilice un relleno de la marca Patrick Cameron adecuado para su color. (véase la página 89).

44

- Attach padding under ponytail and hair grip to back of head.
- Das Polster unter dem Pferdeschwanz befestigen und am Hinterkopf festklemmen.
- Attaccare l'imbottitura sotto la coda di cavallo ed applicare la forcina dietro la testa.
- Fije el relleno debajo de la coleta y sujételo con horquillas en la parte posterior de la cabeza.

- Ensure padding is the shape and size you desire.
- Darauf achten, dass das Polster in Form und Größe Ihren Wünschen entspricht.
- Assicurarsi che l'imbottitura sia della forma e delle dimensioni desiderate.
- Compruebe que el relleno es de la forma y el tamaño deseados.

- Divide ponytail into 2 sections.
- Pferdeschwanz in 2 Teile teilen.
- Dividere la coda di cavallo in 2 sezioni.
- Divida la coleta en 2 partes.

- Brush first section and shape firmly over padding. Twist tail and place under padding.
- Erstes Teil bürsten und fest über das Polster formen. Die Strähne verdrehen und unter das Polster schieben.
- Spazzolare la prima sezione e conferire una forma precisa sopra l'imbottitura. Attorcigliare la coda e collocarla sotto l'imbottitura.
- Cepille la primera parte y sujétela bien sobre el relleno. Enrolle la coleta y colóquela debajo del relleno.

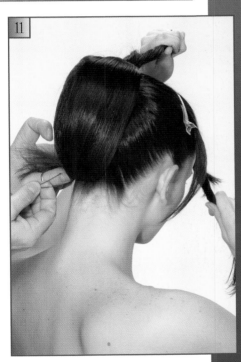

- Hair grip twisted tail at neck.
- Verdrehte Strähne am Hals festklemmen.
- Collocare la forcina sulla coda attorcigliata posta sul collo.
- Sujete con horquillas la coleta enrollada al cuello.

- Hair grip end tail under padding.
- Ende der Strähne unter dem Polster festklemmen.
- Collocare la forcina sulla coda estrema sotto l'imbottitura.
- Sujete con horquillas el extremo de la coleta debajo del relleno.

- Repeat on opposite side.
- Auf gegenüberliegender Seite wiederholen.
- Ripetere l'operazione sul lato opposto.
- Repita la operación en el lado contrario.

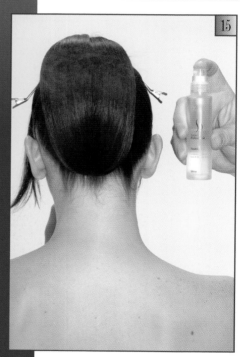

- Spray a little gloss onto bouffante for extra shine.
- Für besonderen Glanz etwas Gloss auf die Bouffante sprühen.
- Spruzzare un po' di lacca sui capelli gonfi per una maggiore brillantezza.
- Aplique un poco de gloss en spray sobre el cardado, para aportarle brillo adicional.

- Brush top area over to left side.
- Oberen Bereich zur linken Seite hinüber kämmen.
- Spazzolare l'area superiore fino al lato sinistro.
- Cepille la parte superior sobre el lado izquierdo.

- Place finger under and loop tail back to create a roll.
- Finger unterschieben und Strähne zu einer Rolle zurück schlingen.
- Collocare il dito al di sotto e girare la coda all'indietro per creare un rotolo.
- Coloque el dedo debajo y retuerza la coleta hacia atrás hasta crear un rollo.

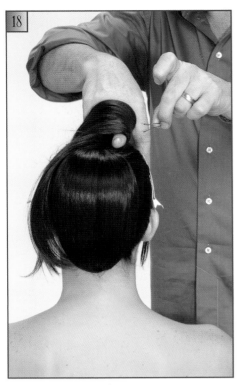

- Hair grip roll to scalp.
- Rolle am Kopf festklemmen.
- Collocare la forcina sul rotolo fino al cuoio capelluto.
- Sujete el rollo con horquillas al cuero cabelludo.

- Hold roll with section clip at front. Place tail toward back.
- Rolle mit Strähnenklemme an Vorderseite befestigen. Strähne nach hinten legen.
- Mantenere il rotolo con la forcina di sezione sulla parte anteriore. Collocare la coda verso la parte posteriore.
- Sujete el rollo en la parte delantera con una pinza. Coloque la coleta en dirección hacia la parte posterior de la cabeza.

- Hair grip tail into base of ponytail.
- Strähne im Ansatz des Pferdeschwanzes festklemmen.
- Collocare la forcina sulla coda nella base della coda di cavallo.
- Sujete la coleta con horquillas en la base de la cola.

- Brush and blend tail over bouffante.
- Strähne bürsten und über Bouffante legen.
- Spazzolare e mescolare la coda sui capelli gonfi.
- Cepille y mezcle la cola sobre el cardado.

- Take tails from step 5.
- Partien aus Schritt 5 nehmen.
- Prelevare le code di cui alla fase 5.
- Use los mechones de cabello mencionados en el paso 5.

- Cross tails over top of bouffante to hide hair grips.
- Die Strähnen zur Abdeckung der Klemmen oben über die Bouffante kreuzen.
- Incrociare le code al di sopra della cima dei capelli gonfi per nascondere le forcine.
- Cruce los mechones por encima del cardado, para ocultar las horquillas.

- Gently place tails around side of bouffante.
- Die Enden vorsichtig rund um die Seite der Bouffante legen.
- Collocare delicatamente le code intorno alla parte laterale dei capelli gonfi.
- Coloque con cuidado los mechones alrededor del lateral del cardado.

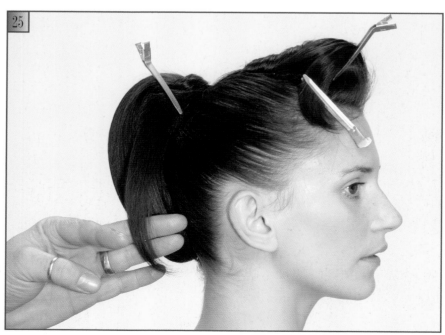

- Repeat on opposite side. • Auf gegenüberliegender Seite wiederholen.
- Ripetere l'operazione sul lato opposto. • Repita la operación en el lado contrario.

- Shape front area and hair spray to hold.
- Vorderen Bereich formen und mit Haarspray Halt geben.
- Conferire una forma precisa all'area anteriore ed applicare lo spray per assicurare la presa.
- Dele forma a la parte delantera y aplique laca para fijar el cabello.

Fun and Funky

Before/Vorher/Prima/Antes

- Create a rectangular section from temple to temple and back to crown. Place remaining hair into a ponytail on crown.
- Eine rechteckige Partie von Schläfe zu Schläfe und zurück zum Scheitel bilden. Das übrige Haar in einem Pferdeschwanz am Scheitel zusammenbinden.
- Creare una sezione rettangolare da tempia a tempia ed all'indietro verso la corona. Raccogliere i capelli rimanenti in una coda di cavallo sulla corona stessa.
- Haga una división rectangular de sien a sien, y hacia atrás en dirección a la coronilla. Haga una cola en la coronilla con el resto del cabello.

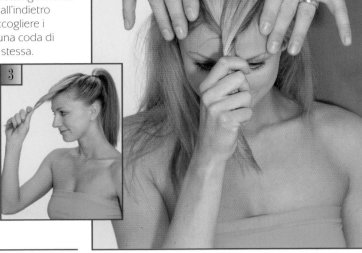

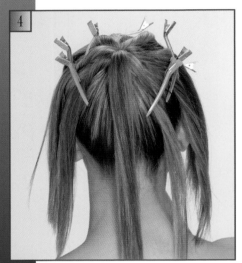

- Divide ponytail into 8 even sections.
- Pferdeschwanz in 8 Teile aufteilen.
- Dividere la coda di cavallo in 8 sezioni identiche.
- Divida la cola en 8 partes parejas.

- Start braiding a loose 3 strand plait on first section.
- Einen lockeren Zopf aus drei Teilen mit der ersten Partie beginnen.
- Iniziare a formare una treccia sciolta a 3 ciocche sulla prima sezione.
- Para empezar, haga en la primera de las partes una trenza poco apretada con 3 mechones.

- Plait out 3 cm, then take out a fine strand of hair from the side of plait.
- 3 cm flechten, dann eine feine Haarsträhne aus der Seite des Zopfes entnehmen.
- Sporgere la treccia di 3 cm., quindi prelevare una ciocca fine di capelli dalla parte laterale della treccia.
- Trence unos 3 cm de cabello, y luego extraiga un fino mechón del lateral de la trenza.

- Every centimetre of the plait remove a fine strand.
- Bei jedem Zentimeter eine feine Strähne aus dem Zopf nehmen.
- Per ogni centimetro di treccia, rimuovere una ciocca fine.
- Cada vez que lleve trenzado un centímetro, saque un mechón fino.

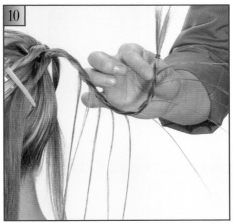

- Place a small band on tail.
- Ein schmales Band um die Strähne binden.
- Collocare una piccola fascia sulla coda.
- Coloque una cinta pequeña en el extremo.

- Complete all 8 sections as in steps 5-10.
- All 8 Partien wie in Schritt 5 bis 10 beschrieben bearbeiten.
- Completare tutte le 8 sezioni come nelle fasi da 5 a 10.
- Haga lo mismo con las 8 partes, siguiendo los pasos 5-10.

- Apply hair gloss to separate each strand.
- Haargloss zur Abteilung jeder Strähne aufbringen.
- Applicare della lacca per separare ogni ciocca.
- Aplique serum para separar los mechones uno por uno.

- Divide top section into four sections from side to side.
- Oberste Partie von einer zur anderen Seite in vier Teile aufteilen.
- Dividere la sezione superiore in quattro sezioni più piccole da lato a lato.
- Divida la parte de arriba en otras cuatro partes de un lado al otro.

- Repeat steps 5-12 on each of the 4 sections.

- Schritte 5 bis 12 mit jeder der 4 Partien wiederholen.

- Ripetere le fasi da 5 a 12 su ognuna delle 4 sezioni.

- Repita los pasos 5-12 en cada una de las 4 partes.

- Completed view of top area.

- Fertiggestellter oberer Bereich.

- Vista completa dell'area superiore.

- Vista de la zona superior terminada.

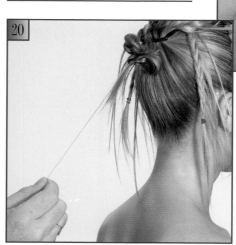

- Take a very very fine strand of hair from tail of braid. Hold strand firmly, place finger and thumb onto elastic and push braid towards the head.

- Eine sehr, sehr feine Haarsträhne aus dem Teil des Zopfes nehmen. Strähne fest halten, Finger und Daumen um Gummiband halten und Zopf zum Kopf hin drücken.

- Prelevare una ciocca finissima di capelli dalla coda alla treccia. Mantenere saldamente ferma la ciocca, collocare il dito e il pollice sull'elastico e spingere la treccia verso la testa.

- Saque un mechón muy finito de cabello del extremo de la trenza. Sujételo con firmeza, coloque el índice y el pulgar en una gomilla y empuje la trenza hacia la cabeza.

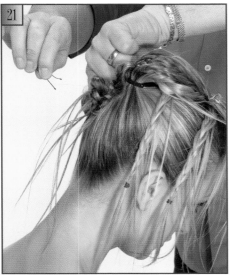

- Ensure strands are on top of braid and hair grip braid 3 cms from ponytail base.

- Darauf achten, dass die Strähnen auf der Oberseite des Zopfes sind und den Zopf 3 cm vom Ansatz des Pferdeschwanzes entfernt festklemmen.

- Assicurarsi che le ciocche siano in cima alle trecce e collocare la forcina sulla treccia a 3 cm. dalla base della coda di cavallo.

- Compruebe que los mechones están en lo alto de la trenza, y sujétela con horquillas a unos 3 cm del lugar de inicio de la cola.

- Repeat steps 19-21 on all 8 braids.

- Schritte 19 bis 21 mit allen 8 Zöpfen wiederholen.

- Ripetere le fasi da 19 a 21 su tutte le 8 trecce.

- Repita los pasos 19-21 en las 8 trenzas.

- Now repeat steps 19 on top 4 sections and place as desired.

- Nun Schritt 19 an den obersten 4 Partien wiederholen und wie gewünscht platzieren.

- Ripetere quindi la fase 19 sulle 4 sezioni superiori e collocare nel modo desiderato.

- Ahora, repita los pasos 19 en lo alto de las 4 partes, y colóquelas como desee.

Loops

Before/Vorher/Prima/Antes

- Section ear to crown to ear and brush lower section back into an asymmetric ponytail Do the same with the top section and place 1 cm above the lower ponytail.

- Haar vom Ohr über den Scheitel zum anderen Ohr abteilen und untere Partie in einen asymmetrischen Pferdeschwanz zurückkämmen. Dasselbe mit der oberen Partie tun und 1 cm über dem unteren Pferdeschwanz ablegen.

- Sezionare da orecchio a corona e da corona a orecchio e spazzolare la sezione inferiore all'indietro in una coda di cavallo asimettrica. Procedere allo stesso modo con la sezione superiore e collocare 1 cm. al di sopra della coda di cavallo inferiore.

- Practique una división oreja-coronilla-oreja y sujete el cabello de la parte inferior en una cola asimétrica. Repita la misma operación con la parte superior dejando 1 cm de separación con la cola inferior.

- Divided top and lower ponytails into 5 sections each.

- Oberen und unteren Pferdeschwanz in je 5 Partien aufteilen.

- Dividere le code di cavallo superiori ed inferiori in 5 sezioni ciascuna.

- Divida las colas superior e inferior en 5 partes cada una.

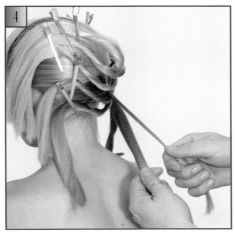

- Starting on the lower ponytail, take the first of your 5 sections and remove a quarter of that section.

- Mit dem unteren Pferdeschwanz beginnend die erste der 5 Partien nehmen und ein Viertel dieser Partie entfernen.

- Iniziando dalla coda di cavallo inferiore, prelevate la prima delle vostre 5 sezioni e rimuovere un quarto di tale sezione.

- Empezando con la cola inferior, extraiga una cuarta parte del cabello de la primera de las 5 partes.

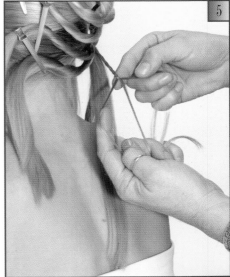

- Using the quarter section plait out 4 cm.

- Mit dem Viertel der Partie 4 cm flechten.

- Usando il quarto di sezione, sporgere la treccia di 4 cm.

- Haga una trenza de 4 cm con esa cuarta parte de cabello.

- Now take a strand of hair from the remaining section below and twist gently.

- Jetzt eine Strähne der übrigen unteren Partie nehmen und sanft verdrehen.

- Prelevare ora una ciocca di capelli dalla sezione rimanente al di sotto ed attorcigliare con delicatezza.

- A continuación, saque un mechón de cabello del resto de la coleta de abajo y enróllelo con suavidad.

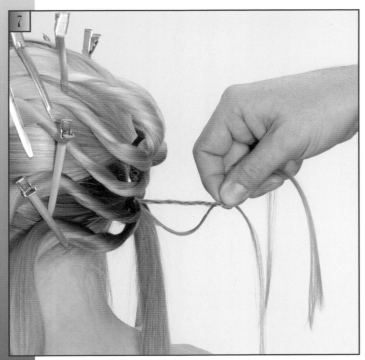

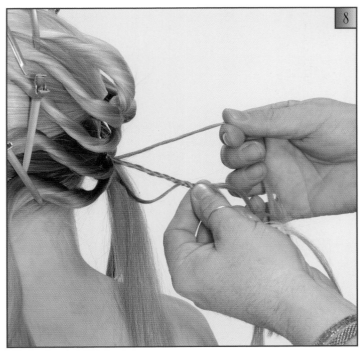

- Place this twist into the plait and plait out 1 cm before adding in the next strand from below.

- Diese verdrehte Strähne in den Zopf legen und 1 cm weiter flechten, dann die nächste Strähne von unten dazunehmen.

- Collocare tale attorcigliamento nella treccia e sporgere quest'ultima di 1 cm. prima di aggiungere la ciocca successiva dal di sotto.

- Introduzca este rollo en la trenza y tréncelo 1 cm antes de añadir el siguiente mechón de abajo.

- Take another strand from below, twist and add into plait.

- Eine weitere Strähne von unten nehmen, verdrehen und in den Zopf einflechten.

- Prelevare un'altra ciocca dal di sotto, attorcigliare ed aggiungere alla treccia.

- Saque otro mechón de abajo, enróllelo y agréguelo a la trenza.

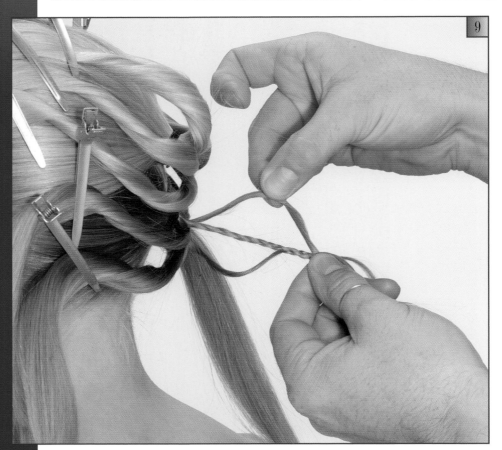

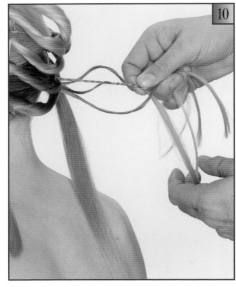

- Continue process till end of plait ensuring you have 3 loops on either side of the plait.

- Den Vorgang bis zum Ende des Zopfes fortsetzen, dabei darauf achten, dass auf jeder Seite des Zopfes 3 Schleifen entstehen.

- Continuare l'operazione fino all'estremità della treccia assicurandosi di avere 3 curve su ciascun lato di quest'ultima.

- Siga con esta operación hasta acabar la trenza, comprobando que haya 3 bucles a cada lado de la trenza.

- Creating soft loops as shown. • Weiche Schleifen wie gezeigt herstellen.

- Creare curve morbide nel modo indicato. • Cree bucles suaves de la forma descrita.

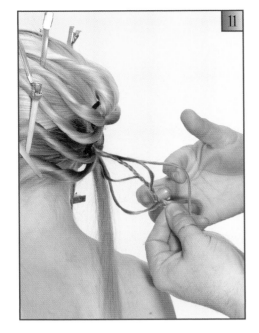

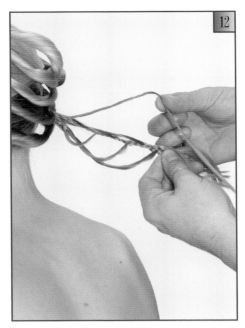

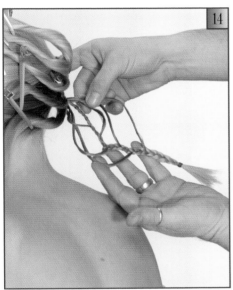

- Completed section.
- Fertiger Abschnitt.
- Sezione completa.
- Parte terminada.

- Lower 5 sections completed.
- Untere 5 Partien fertig gestellt.
- Le 5 sezioni inferiori complete.
- 5 partes inferiores terminadas.

- Upper 5 sections completed.
- Obere 5 Partien fertig gestellt.
- Le 5 sezioni superiori complete.
- 5 partes superiores terminadas.

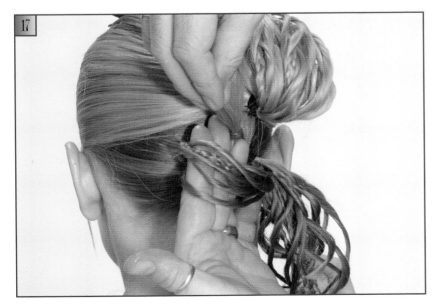

- Take first of the 5 lower sections, wrap around fingers, creating a barrel curl and hair grip to side of lower pony tail base.

- Die erste der fünf unteren Partien nehmen, um die Finger wickeln, eine Barrel-Locke machen und zur Seite des Ansatzes des unteren Pferdeschwanzes festklemmen.

- Prelevare la prima delle 5 sezioni inferiore, avvolgere intorno alle dita creando un ricciolo cilindrico e collocare la forcina sulla parte laterale della base della coda di cavallo inferiore.

- Envuelva la primera de las 5 partes inferiores alrededor de los dedos, para crear un rizo en forma de cilindro, y sujétela con horquillas en el lateral de la base de la cola inferior.

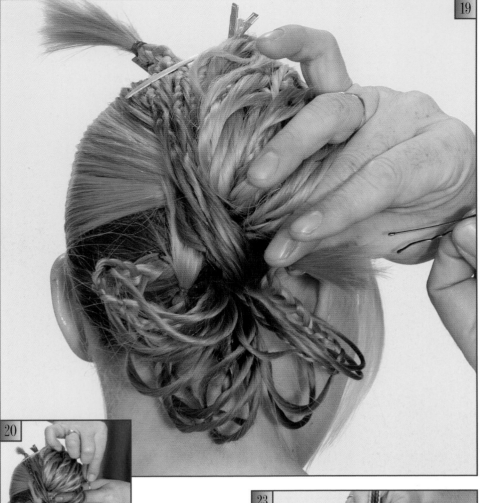

- Repeat process working around base of ponytail on next 3 lower sections.
- Vorgang wiederholen, indem rund um den Ansatz des Pferdeschwanzes an den 3 nächsten unteren Partien gearbeitet wird.
- Ripetere l'operazione lavorando intorno alla base della coda di cavallo sulle 3 sezioni inferiori successive.
- Repita la operación alrededor de la base de la cola en las otras 3 partes inferiores.

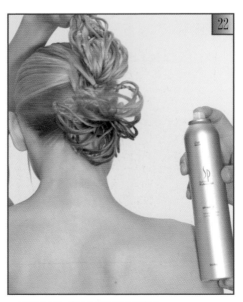

- Place fifth lower section on top, to fill the centre of the shape.
- Fünfte untere Partie nach oben legen, um die Mitte der Form auszufüllen.
- Collocare in cima la quinta sezione inferiore per riempire il centro della forma.
- Coloque la quinta parte inferior en lo alto, de forma que quede en el centro.

- Hair spray for hold and shine.
- Haarspray für Glanz und Halt.
- Applicare lo spray per assicurare la presa e la brillantezza.
- Aplique laca para aportar brillo y fijación al cabello.

- Repeat steps 4-22 on the top ponytail. Place front as desired. If desired, place small flowers inside each of the barrel curl bases.
- Schritte 4 bis 22 mit dem oberen Pferdeschwanz wiederholen. Vorderseite wie gewünscht legen. Wenn gewünscht, kleine Blumen in den Ansatz jeder Barrel-Locke stecken.
- Ripetere le operazioni da 4 a 22 sulla coda di cavallo superiore. Collocare la parte anteriore nel modo voluto. Se lo si desidera, collocare piccoli fiori all'interno di ciascuna base di ricciolo cilindrico.
- Repita los pasos 4-22 en la cola de arriba. Coloque la parte delantera como desee. Si lo prefiere, coloque flores pequeñas dentro de cada uno de los rizos en forma de cilindro.

Fingerwave Renaissance

- Before – Hair needs to be very wet before starting. Create a side parting.
- Vorher – Haar muss vor Beginn sehr feucht sein. Einen Seitenscheitel ziehen.
- Prima – I capelli devono essere molto bagnati prima di iniziare. Creare un punto di separazione laterale.
- Antes – El cabello tiene que estar muy húmedo antes de empezar. Péinelo con la raya al lado.

- Place a strong gel onto hands.
- Ein starkes Gel auf die Hände geben.
- Collocare una gran quantità di gel sulle mani.
- Extiéndase por las manos un gel fuerte.

- Massage gel into root area. Important – Roots area must be saturated in gel for successful finger wave.
- Gel in den Wurzelbereich einmassieren. Wichtig – der Wurzelbereich muss für eine erfolgreiche Fingerwelle mit Gel gesättigt sein.
- Massaggiare con gel nell'area delle radici. Importante: tale area deve essere saturo di gel per una successiva ondulazione con il dito eseguita in modo positivo.
- Aplique el gel con un masaje por la zona de las raíces. Esta zona tiene que tener bastante gel para que las ondas con los dedos salgan bien.

- Comb product through hair to distribute evenly.
- Das Produkt zur gleichmäßigen Verteilung durchs Haar kämmen.
- Passare il prodotto con il pettine per i capelli in modo da distribuire in modo uniforme.
- Distribuya el producto con un peine de forma uniforme por todo el cabello.

- Starting at side parting use a cutting comb to scrape towards the face. Press finger firmly on scalp behind wave crest to create first wave.
- An der Seite beginnen und einen Schneidekamm zum Formen zum Gesicht hin verwenden. Finger fest auf den Kopf hinter dem Wellenkamm drücken und somit erste Welle herstellen.
- Iniziando dal punto di divisione laterale, utilizzare un pettine tagliente per raschiare verso il viso. Premere con forza il dito sul cuoio capelluto dietro la cresta d'onda per creare la prima ondulazione.
- Comenzando por la raya al lado, utilice un peine fino para arrastrar hacia la cara. Presione con fuerza el índice en el cuero cabelludo detrás de la cresta de la onda para crear la primera onda.

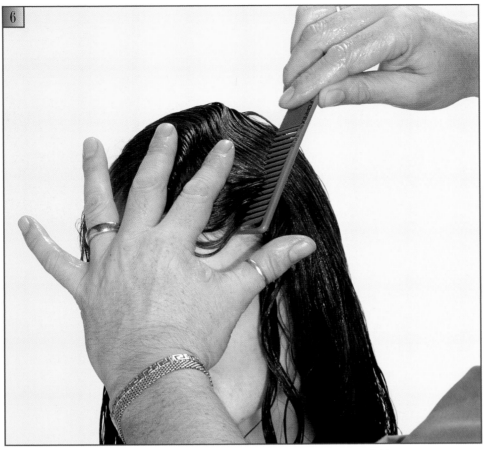

- Pinch wave crest between both fingers and scrape hair back, creating an S-shape.
- Wellenkamm kurz zwischen beide Finger klemmen und Haar zurückbürsten, dadurch eine S-Form bilden.
- Serrare la cresta d'onda tra le due dita e raschiare i capelli all'indietro creando una forma ad S.
- Apriete la cresta de la onda entre ambos dedos índices y vaya arrastrando el cabello hacia atrás formando una S.

- Section clip into wave at front to hold.
- Zum Fixieren Welle vorn mit Clip festklemmen.
- Collocare una forcina di sezione nell'ondulazione sulla parte anteriore in modo da assicurare la presa.
- Coloque una pinza en la onda de la parte delantera para sujetarla.

- Repeat process down side of head. Do not lift comb off scalp, applying constant pressure. Work from side to side in S-shaped waves, pinching wave crests between fingers.
- Vorgang entlang der Kopfseite nach unten wiederholen. Den Kamm nicht vom Kopf heben, konstanten Druck ausüben. Von einer Seite zur anderen in S-förmigen Wellen arbeiten, dabei die Wellenkämme kurz zwischen die Finger klemmen.
- Ripetere il processo sulla parte laterale della testa. Non sollevare il pettine fuori dal cuoio capelluto applicando una pressione costante. Lavorare da lato a lato in ondulazioni a forma di S, serrando le creste d'onda tra le dita.
- Repita la operación con la parte inferior de la cabeza. No levante el peine del cuero cabelludo, y aplique una presión constante. Trabaje de lado a lado en ondas en forma de S, apretando las crestas de ola entre los índices.

- Place section clips into waves at front and behind ear to hold.
- Zur Fixierung Clips an der Vorderseite und hinter dem Ohr in die Welle klemmen.
- Collocare forcine di sezione nelle ondulazioni sulla parte anteriore e dietro l'orecchio per assicurare la presa.
- Coloque pinzas en las ondas para sujetarlas, en la parte delantera y detrás de la oreja.

- Repeat steps 5-10 on opposite side.
- Schritte 5 bis 10 auf der anderen Seite wiederholen.
- Ripetere le fasi da 5 a 10 sul lato opposto.
- Repita los pasos 5-10 en el otro lado.

- Diffuser dry front hair to set gel.
- Haar vorn mit Diffuser trocknen, um Gel zu festigen.
- Diffusore: asciugare i capelli anteriori per applicare il gel.
- Seque el cabello utilizando difusor, para que haga efecto el gel.

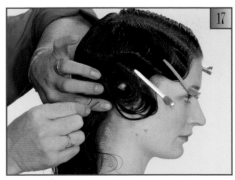

- Hair grip end of wave behind ear on both sides.
- Ende der Welle auf beiden Seiten hinter dem Ohr festklemmen.
- Collocare la forcina sull'estremità dell'ondulazione dietro l'orecchio su entrambi i lati.
- Sujete con horquillas el extremo de la onda detrás de ambos lados de la oreja.

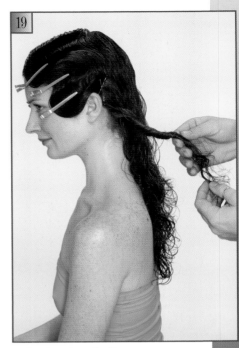

- Gently twist tail of last wave.
- Ende der letzten Welle sanft verdrehen.
- Attorcigliare con delicatezza la coda dell'ultima ondulazione.
- Enrolle un poco el extremo de la última onda.

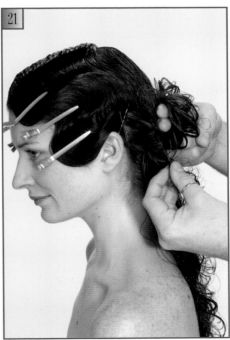

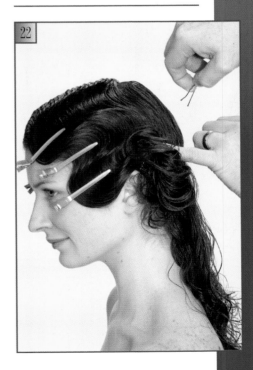

- Pull gently along twist to create texture.
- Verdrehte Strähne sanft zupfen, um Struktur zu schaffen.
- Tirare delicatamente lungo l'attorcigliamento per creare consistenza.
- Tire un poco del rollo para crear textura.

- Roll around 2 fingers and hair grip into place. Repeat on other side.
- Um zwei Finger wickeln und an richtiger Stelle festklemmen. Auf der anderen Seite wiederholen
- Fare rotolare intorno a 2 dita e collocare la forcina nella posizione corretta.
- Enróllelo en 2 dedos y sujételo en su sitio con horquillas. Repita la operación en el otro lado.

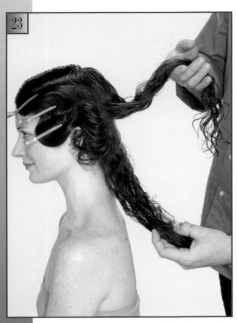

- Divide back area into 2 horizontal sections.
- Hinteren Bereich in 2 waagerechte Partien aufteilen.
- Dividere l'area posteriore in 2 sezioni orizzontali.
- Divida la zona de atrás en 2 partes horizontales.

- Divide lower section into 3. Start in middle, twist gently and pull along twist to create texture.
- Untere Partie in 3 Teile teilen. In der Mitte beginnend sanft verdrehen und für Textur entlang der verdrehten Haare zupfen.
- Dividere la sezione inferiore in 3 sezioni più piccole. Iniziare dal centro, attorcigliare delicatamente e tirare lungo l'attorcigliamento per creare consistenza.
- Divida la parte inferior en 3. Comience en el medio, enrolle un poco el cabello y tire para crear textura.

- Roll around 2 fingers and hair grip into place.
- Um zwei Finger wickeln und an richtiger Stelle festklemmen.
- Far rotolare intorno a 2 dita e collocare la forcina in posizione corretta.
- Enróllelo en 2 dedos y sujételo en su sitio con horquillas.

- All 3 twists completed.
- Alle 3 verdrehten Strähnen sind fertig.
- Tutti e 3 gli attorcigliamenti completi.
- Los 3 rollos terminados.

- Divide top section into 4 and repeat process.
- Obere Partie in 4 Teile teilen und Vorgang wiederholen.
- Dividere la sezione superiore in 4 sezioni più piccole e ripetere l'operazione.
- Divida la parte superior en 4 y repita la operación.

Textured Chignon

Before/Vorher/Prima/Antes

- Take a 2 cm diagonal strip from crown to face.
- Einen 2 cm breiten diagonalen Streifen vom Scheitel zum Gesicht nehmen.
- Prelevare una striscia diagonale di 2 cm. dalla corona al viso.
- Peine una franja de cabello de 2 cm en diagonal, de la coronilla a la cara.

- Scalp braid hair loosely from crown to front.
- Haar lose in einen Bauernzopf vom Scheitel nach vorn flechten.
- Collocare in modo sciolto dalla corona alla parte anteriore i capelli delle trecce poste sul cuoio capelluto.
- Haga una trenza de espiga poco apretada desde la coronilla a la parte delantera.

- Place all other hair into a low ponytail at neck.
- Alle anderen Haare in einen niedrigen Pferdeschwanz am Hals zusammenbinden.
- Raccogliere tutti gli altri capelli in una coda di cavallo bassa sul collo.
- Sujete el resto del cabello en una cola baja en el cuello.

- Braid up on a 45 degree angle to create a soft front.
- In einem 45°-Winkel aufwärts flechten, um eine weiche Front zu schaffen.
- Intrecciare su un angolo di 45 gradi per creare una parte anteriore morbida.
- Trence el cabello en un ángulo de 45 grados, para crear una parte delantera suave.

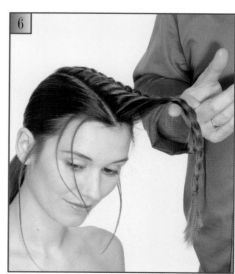

- Place band on end.
- Am Ende mit Band abschließen.
- Collocare la fascia sull'estremità.
- Coloque una cinta en el extremo.

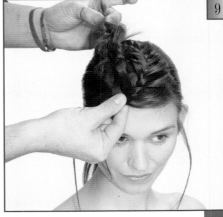

- Pull at each rib of braid to create soft texture.
- An jedem Teil des Zopfes zupfen, um sanfte Struktur zu schaffen.
- Tirare ogni cresta di treccia per creare una consistenza morbida.
- Tire de cada extremo de la trenza para crear una textura suave.

- Take braid around and back and hair grip into scalp braid and into ponytail base.
- Zopf rundum und zurück nehmen und am Bauernzopf und im Pferdeschwanzansatz festklemmen
- Spostare la treccia intorno e all'indietro e collocare la forcina nella treccia posta sul cuoio capelluto e nella base della coda di cavallo.
- Tire de la trenza hacia atrás y sujétela con horquillas en la trenza de espiga y en la base de la cola.

- Divide ponytail into 8 even sections.
- Pferdeschwanz in 8 gleiche Teile aufteilen.
- Dividere la coda di cavallo in 8 sezioni identiche.
- Divida la cola en 8 partes similares.

- Create a **loose** 2 strand braid by taking a small section from the left side and placing it into the right side.
- Eine **lose** Haarflechte aus 2 Strähnen flechten, indem eine kleine Partie von der linken Seite genommen und in die rechte Seite eingefügt wird.
- Creare una treccia **sciolta** a 2 ciocche prelevando una piccola sezione dal lato sinistro e collocandola sul lato destro.
- Haga una trenza **poco apretada** de 2 mechones introduciendo algo de cabello del lado izquierdo en el lado derecho.

- Repeat process by taking a small section from the right side and crossing it over and into the left side.
- Vorgang wiederholen, indem eine kleine Partie von der rechten Seite genommen, überkreuzt und in die linke Seite eingefügt wird.
- Ripetere l'operazione prelevando una piccola sezione dal lato destro ed incrociandola al di sopra e all'interno del lato sinistro.
- Repita la operación trenzando esta vez algo de cabello del lado derecho con el lado izquierdo.

- Take another small section from the left side and place it into the right side.
- Eine weitere kleine Strähne von der linken Seite nehmen und in die rechte Seite einfügen.
- Prelevare un'altra piccola sezione dal lato sinistro e collocarla nel lato destro.
- Vuelva a introducir algo de cabello del lado izquierdo en el lado derecho.

- Repeat process by taking a small section from the right side and crossing it over and into the left side.
- Vorgang wiederholen, indem eine kleine Partie von der rechten Seite genommen, überkreuzt und in die linke Seite eingefügt wird.
- Ripetere l'operazione prelevando una piccola sezione dal lato destro ed incrociandola al di sopra e all'interno del lato sinistro.
- Repita la operación trenzando esta vez algo de cabello del lado derecho con el lado izquierdo.

- Continue until end and place band to hold.
- Bis zum Ende fortsetzen und mit Gummiband befestigen.
- Continuare fino alla fine e collocare la fascia per assicurare la presa.
- Siga trenzando hasta terminar, y sujete el cabello con una cinta.

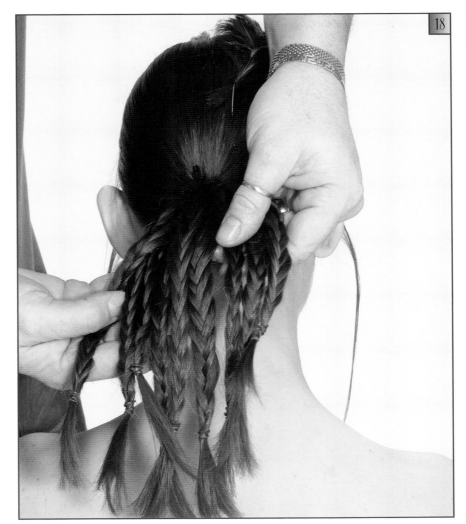

- 8 Completed braids. • 8 fertige Zöpfe. • 8 Trecce complete. • 8 Trenzas terminadas.

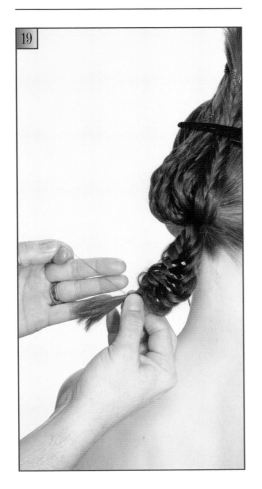

- Take a very very fine strand of hair from tail of braid. Hold strand firmly, place finger and thumb onto elastic and push braid towards the head.
- Eine sehr, sehr feine Haarsträhne aus dem Teil des Zopfes nehmen. Strähne fest halten, Finger und Daumen um Gummiband halten und Zopf zum Kopf hin drücken.
- Prelevare una ciocca di capelli finissima dalla coda della treccia. Mantenere saldamente ferma la ciocca, collocare il dito ed il pollice sull'elastico e spingere la treccia verso la testa.
- Extraiga un mechón muy fino de cabello del extremo de la trenza. Sujete bien el mechón, coloque el índice y el pulgar en una gomilla y empuje la trenza en dirección a la cabeza.

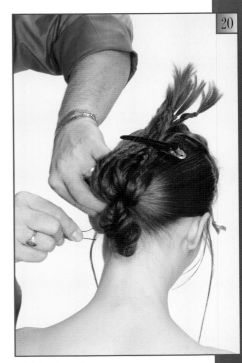

- Hair grip at base.
- An Ansatz festklemmen.
- Collocare la forcina sulla base.
- Sujete el cabello con horquillas a la base.

- Gently pull at braid to create soft curls and loops.
- Leicht am Zopf zupfen, um sanfte Schleifen und Locken zu schaffen.
- Tirare con delicatezza la treccia per creare riccioli e curve morbidi.
- Tire un poco de la trenza para crear rizos y bucles suaves.

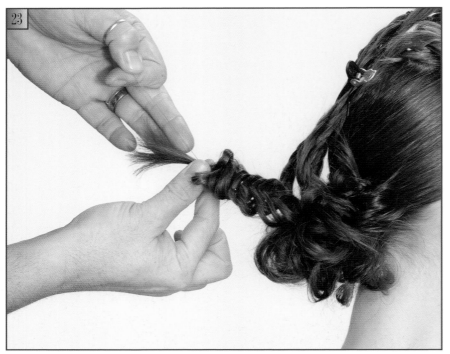

- Repeat steps 19-21 on remaining braids building shape as you go.
- Schritte 19 bis 21 an den übrigen Zöpfen wiederholen und im Laufe der Arbeit die Form aufbauen.
- Ripetere le fasi da 19 a 21 sulle rimanenti trecce conferendo via via la forma.
- Repita los pasos 19-21 con el resto de las trenzas, hasta lograr la forma deseada.

- Hide tails under chignon.
- Strähnen unter Chignon verstecken
- Nascondere le code sotto lo chignon.
- Oculte los extremos por debajo del moño.

Classic Chignon

Before/Vorher/Prima/Antes

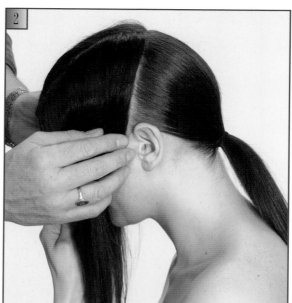

- Section from ear to crown to ear. Place back section into a low ponytail.
- Von einem Ohr über den Scheitel bis zum anderen Ohr abteilen. Partie in einen tiefen Pferdeschwanz binden.
- Sezionare dall'orecchio alla corona e dalla corona all'orecchio. Collocare la sezione posteriore in una coda di cavallo bassa.
- Practique una división oreja-coronilla-oreja. Sujete la parte de atrás del cabello en una cola baja.

- Divide front into 3 sections.
- Vorderseite in 3 Partien aufteilen.
- Dividere la parte anteriore in 3 sezioni.
- Divida la zona delantera en 3 partes.

- Take Patrick Cameron hair padding (see page 89) and shape into a semi circle.
- Patrick Cameron Haarpolster nehmen (siehe Seite 89) und in einem Halbkreis formen.
- Prelevare l'imbottitura per capelli Patrick Cameron (vedere alla pagina 89) e formare un semicerchio.
- Utilice relleno de cabello de la marca Patrick Cameron (véase la página 89) y forme con él un semicírculo.

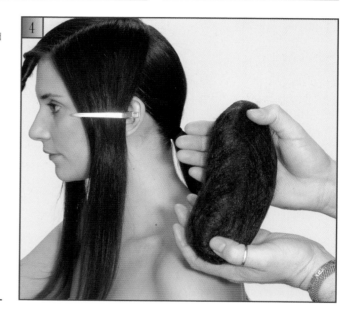

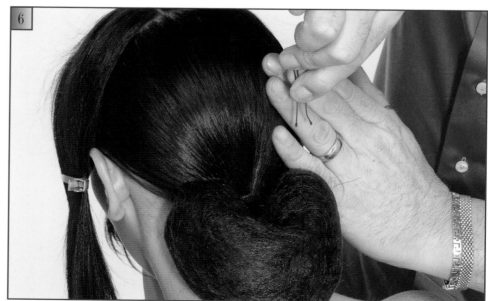

- Hair grip padding to either side of ponytail.
- Polster auf jeder Seite des Schwanzes festklemmen.
- Collocare la forcina sull'imbottitura da entrambi i lati della coda di cavallo.
- Sujete el relleno con horquillas a ambos lados de la cola.

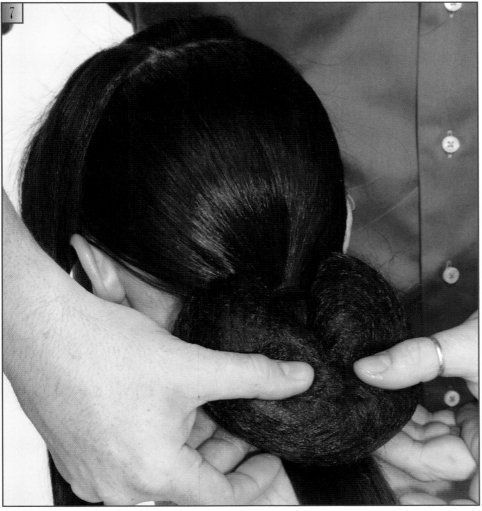

- Check shape is round and even. • Auf runde und gleichmäßige Form achten.
- Controllare che la forma sia circolare ed uniforme. • Compruebe que la forma es redonda y uniforme.

- Divide ponytail into 3 sections.
- Pferdeschwanz in 3 Teile aufteilen.
- Dividere la coda di cavallo in 3 sezioni.
- Divida la cola en 3 partes.

- Place middle section up and over padding in a fan shape to cover and hair grip into ponytail base.
- Das mittlere Teil in Fächerform nach oben und zur Abdeckung über das Polster legen und mit Haarklemmen im Ansatz des Schwanzes befestigen.
- Collocare la sezione centrale in alto ed al di sopra dell'imbottitura a forma di ventilatore in modo da coprire e da collocare la forcina nella base della coda di cavallo.
- Coloque la parte central sobre el relleno y levantada, formando un abanico, y sujétela con horquillas a la base de la cola.

- Repeat with left section.
- Mit linker Partie wiederholen.
- Ripetere l'operazione con la sezione sinistra.
- Repita la operación con la parte izquierda.

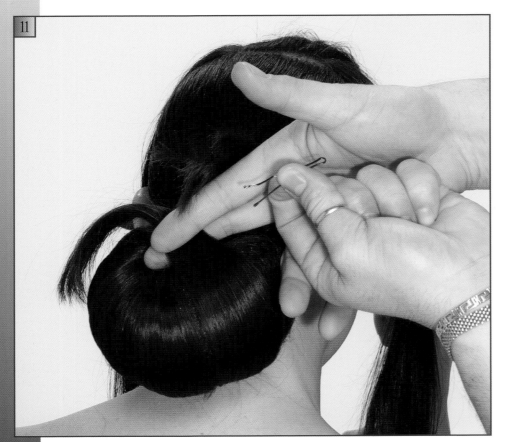

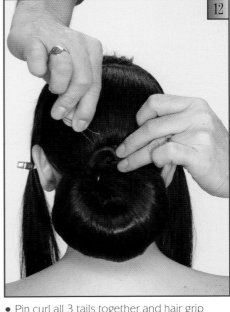

- Repeat with right section. • Mit rechter Partie wiederholen.
- Ripetere l'operazione con la sezione destra. • Repita la operación con la parte derecha.

- Pin curl all 3 tails together and hair grip deep inside padding base.
- Alle 3 Partien gelockt zusammen stecken und tief im Ansatz des Polsters festklemmen.
- Fissare insieme tutte le 3 code arricciandole e collocare la forcina profondamente all'interno della base dell'imbottitura.
- Una con un pin los 3 extremos y sujételos con horquillas en el interior de la base del relleno.

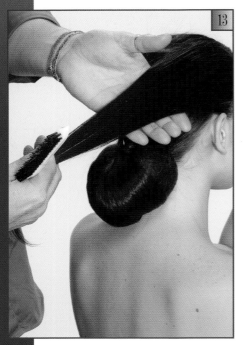

- Brush front right side back to roll.
- Rechte Vorderseite zurück zur Rolle kämmen.
- Spazzolare all'indietro il lato anteriore destro per rotolare.
- Cepille el lateral de la parte delantera derecha hacia atrás para que quede enrollado.

- Hair grip at base and brush tails over opposite side to cover hair padding.
- Am Ansatz festklemmen und Strähnen zur Abdeckung des Polsters über die gegenüberliegende Seite bürsten.
- Collocare la forcina sulla base e spazzolare le code al di sopra del lato opposto per coprire l'imbottitura dei capelli.
- Sujetar con una horquilla a la base y cepille los extremos por encima del lado contrario para tapar el relleno de cabello.

- Hide tails and hair grip under padding to hold.
- Strähnen und Haarklemmen zur Befestigung unter dem Polster verstecken.
- Nascondere le code e collocare la forcina sotto l'imbottitura per assicurare la presa.
- Oculte los extremos y sujételos con horquillas debajo del relleno.

- Repeat on opposite side. • Auf gegenüberliegender Seite wiederholen.
- Ripetere l'operazione sul lato opposto. • Repita lo mismo en el lado contrario.

- To secure tension of left and right side place 2 hair grips vertically down just above ponytail.
- Um die Spannung der rechten und linken Seite zu sichern, 2 Haarklemmen direkt oberhalb des Pferdeschwanzes senkrecht nach unten stecken.
- Per assicurare la tensione dei lati destro e sinistro, collocare verticalmente in basso 2 forcine appena al di sopra della coda di cavallo.
- Para que los lados derecho e izquierdo queden tirantes, sujételos con 2 horquillas mirando hacia abajo, justo encima de la cola.

- Brush top area over and down to chignon.
- Oberen Bereich darüber und nach unten zum Chignon kämmen.
- Spazzolare l'area superiore al di sopra e al di sotto fino allo chignon.
- Cepille la zona de arriba hacia el moño.

- Twist tails and hair grip to hold.
- Die Strähnen verdrehen und mit Haarklemmen befestigen.
- Attorcigliare le code e collocare la forcina per assicurare la presa.
- Ondule los extremos y sujete con horquillas.

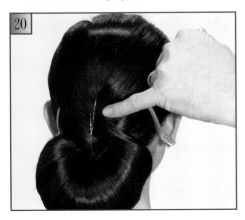

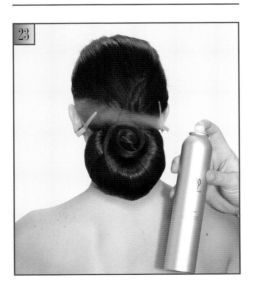

- Create a flat curl with tails of twist and spray to hold.
- Eine flache Locke aus den Strähnen der verdrehten Flechte bilden und mit Haarspray fixieren.
- Creare un ricciolo piatto con code di attorcigliamento ed applicare lo spray per assicurare la presa.
- Cree un rizo plano con los extremos de la onda y aplique laca para aportar fijación.

Trendy Casual

Before/Vorher/Prima/Antes

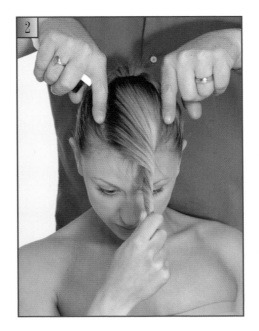

- Create a rectangular section from temple to temple and back to crown. Place remaining hair into a ponytail below crown.
- Eine rechteckige Partie von Schläfe zu Schläfe und zurück zum Scheitel bilden. Das übrige Haar in einem Pferdeschwanz unterhalb des Scheitels zusammenbinden.
- Creare una sezione rettangolare da tempia a tempia ed all'indietro verso la corona. Raccogliere i capelli rimanenti in una coda di cavallo sotto la corona.
- Practique una división rectangular de sien a sien, y hacia atrás en dirección a la coronilla. Haga una cola en la coronilla con el resto del cabello.

- Divide ponytail in 6 and use a large hot tong to give soft movement.
- Pferdeschwanz in 6 Teile teilen und mit einem großen heißen Lockenstab sanfte Bewegung einarbeiten.
- Dividere la coda di cavallo in 6 parti ed utilizzare una molletta calda di grandi dimensioni per conferire un movimento dolce.
- Divida la cola en 6 y utilice unas tenacillas calientes para aportar algo de movimiento.

- Divide front area into 5 sections and hot tong to give soft movement.
- Vorderseite in 5 Partien teilen und mit einem heißen Lockenstab sanfte Bewegung einarbeiten.
- Dividere l'area anteriore in 5 sezioni e collocare una molletta calda per conferire un movimento dolce.
- Divida la zona delantera en 5 partes y aplíqueles unas tenacillas calientes para aportar algo de movimiento.

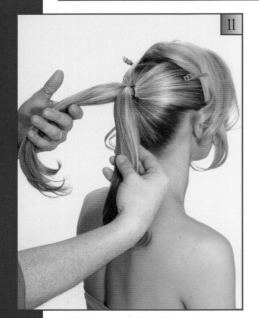

- Divide ponytail into 2 sections.
- Pferdeschwanz in 2 Teile teilen.
- Dividere la coda di cavallo in 2 sezioni.
- Divida la cola en 2 partes.

- Gently twist first section over to right.
- Das erste Teil sanft nach rechts herüber drehen.
- Attorcigliare delicatamente la prima sezione verso destra.
- Ondule con suavidad la primera parte hacia la derecha.

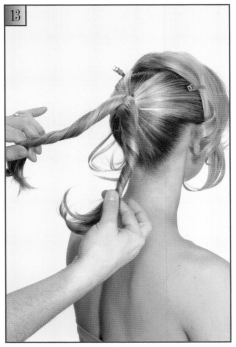

- Gently twist second section over to right.
- Das zweite Teil sanft nach rechts herüber drehen.
- Attorcigliare delicatamente la seconda sezione verso destra.
- Ondule con suavidad la segunda parte hacia la derecha.

- Cross right section over left continuing to twist hair.
- Rechte Partie über die linke kreuzen und das Haar weiter verdrehen.
- Incrociare la sezione destra al di sopra della sinistra continuando ad attorcigliare i capelli.
- Cruce la parte de la derecha sobre la izquierda y siga ondulando el cabello.

- Then right section under left.
- Dann die rechte Partie unter die linke legen.
- Collocare quindi la sezione destra sotto la sezione sinistra.
- A continuación, cruce la parte derecha bajo la izquierda.

- Then right section over left.
- Dann die rechte Partie über die linke legen.
- Successivamente, collocare la sezione destra sopra la sezione sinistra.
- A continuación, cruce la parte derecha sobre la izquierda.

- Continue to end.
- Bis zum Ende fortsetzen.
- Continuare fino alla fine.
- Siga con esta operación hasta terminar.

- Pull at gently twist to create soft loops.
- Vorsichtig an der Flechte zupfen, um weiche Schleifen zu ziehen.
- Tirare delicatamente l'attorcigliamento per creare curve morbide.
- Tire un poco de la onda para crear bucles suaves.

79

- Hair spray twisted texture to hold.
- Die verdrehte Struktur mit Haarspray fixieren.
- Applicare lo spray sulla consistenza attorcigliata per assicurare la presa.
- Aplique laca a las ondas para aportar fijación.

- Pull all around twist gently to create soft loops.
- Die Flechte sanft herum ziehen, um weiche Schleifen zu schaffen.
- Tirare con delicatezza tutt'intorno all'attorcigliamento per creare curve morbide.
- Tire un poco alrededor de la onda para crear bucles suaves.

- Wrap textured twist around and over base.
- Die strukturierte Flechte um und über den Ansatz wickeln.
- Avvolgere l'attorcigliamento provvisto di consistenza intorno e al di sopra della base.
- Envuelva alrededor la onda y encima de la base.

- Hair grip into place.
- Mit Haarklemme befestigen.
- Collocare la forcina nella posizione corretta.
- Coloque las horquillas en su sitio.

- Place front section softly over back.
- Vorderabschnitt sanft über den hinteren legen.
- Collocare delicatamente la sezione anteriore al di sopra di quella posteriore.
- Peine la parte delantera con cuidado hacia atrás.

- Continue placing front area as desired.
- Weiter die Front wie gewünscht legen.
- Continuare a collocare l'area anteriore come desiderato.
- Acabe de peinar la zona delantera a su gusto.

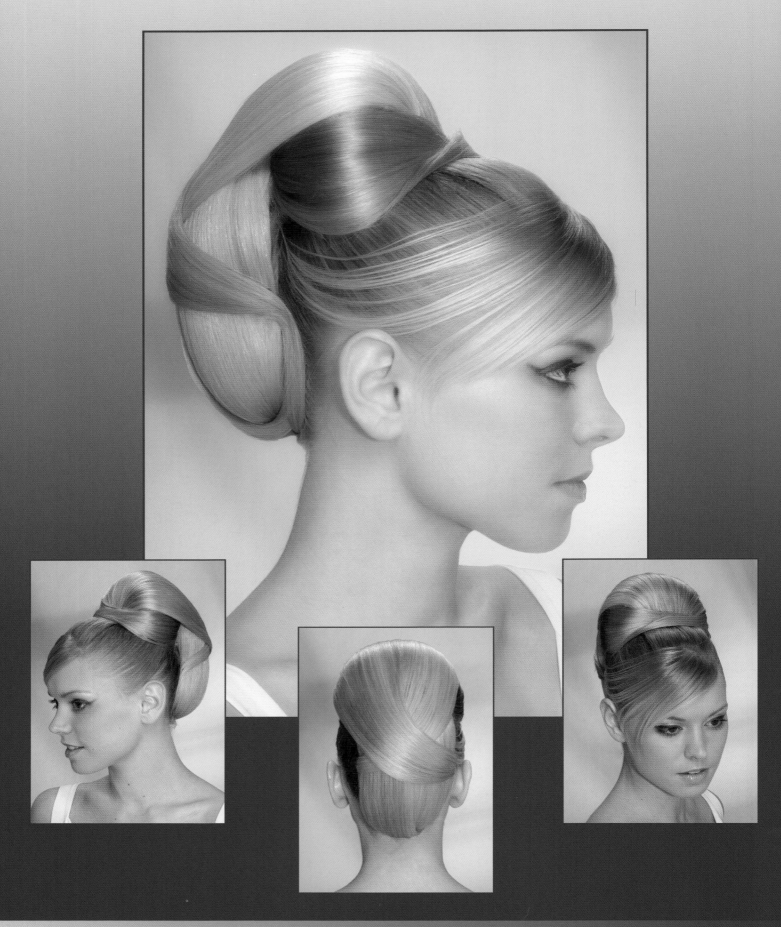

Diva

Before/Vorher/Prima/Antes

- Create a rectangular section from temple to temple and back to crown. Place remaining hair into a ponytail at crown.
- Eine rechteckige Partie von Schläfe zu Schläfe und zurück zum Scheitel bilden. Das übrige Haar in einem Pferdeschwanz am Scheitel zusammenbinden.
- Creare una sezione rettangolare da tempia a tempia ed all'indietro verso la corona. Raccogliere i capelli rimanenti in una coda di cavallo sulla corona stessa.
- Practique una división rectangular de sien a sien, y hacia atrás en dirección a la coronilla. Haga una cola en la coronilla con el resto del cabello.

- Take a quarter of the ponytail from underneath.
- Ein Viertel des Pferdeschwanzes von unten entnehmen.
- Prelevare un quarto della coda di cavallo dal di sotto.
- Extraiga una cuarta parte de la cola de la parte inferior.

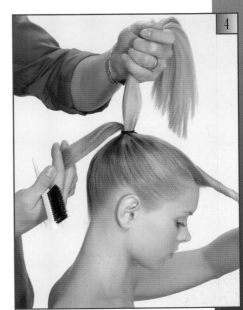

- Divide this quarter section in two and hold with section clips on either side of ear. (These sections will be used in steps 18-20)
- Dieses Viertel in zwei Strähnen teilen und mit Strähnenclips an jeder Seite des Ohrs befestigen. (Diese Partien werden in den Schritten 18 bis 20 verwendet)
- Dividere tale quarto di sezione in due parti ed assicurare la presa con forcine di sezione su entrambi i lati dell'orecchio (tali sezioni saranno usate nelle fasi da 18 a 20).
- Divida esta cuarta parte en dos y sujétela con pinzas a cada lado de la oreja. (Estos mechones se usarán en los pasos 18-20)

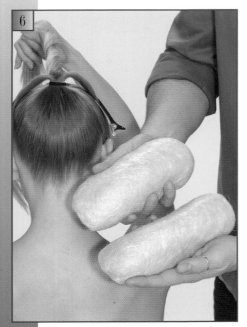

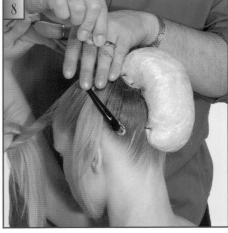

- Take 2 Patrick Cameron hair paddings (see page 89).

- 2 Patrick Cameron Haarpolster nehmen (siehe Seite 89).

- Prelevare 2 imbottiture per capelli Patrick Cameron hair paddings (vedere alla pagina 89).

- Utilice 2 rellenos de cabello de la marca Patrick Cameron (véase la página 89).

Place padding behind ponytail and hair grip firstly to nape of neck.

- Polster hinter den Pferdeschwanz legen und zuerst am Nacken festklemmen.

- Collocare l'imbottitura sotto la coda di cavallo e collocare dapprima la forcina verso la nuca.

- Coloque el relleno detrás de la cola y sujételo con horquillas a la nuca.

- If necessary fold top of padding under to create smaller shape and hair grip padding at base of ponytail.

- Falls erforderlich Oberteil des Polsters falten und damit eine kleinere Form bilden, dann Polster am Ansatz des Pferdeschwanzes festklemmen.

- Se necessario, piegare l'estremità superiore dell'imbottitura al di sotto in modo da creare una forma più piccola e collocare la forcina sull'imbottitura alla base della coda di cavallo.

- Si es necesario, doble la parte superior del relleno por debajo para crear una forma más pequeña y sujete el relleno con horquillas a la base de la cola.

- Place second padding at front of ponytail and shape into a semi circle.

- Zweites Polster an Vorderseite des Pferdeschwanzes legen und in Halbkreis formen.

- Collocare la seconda imbottitura sulla parte anteriore della coda di cavallo e creare una forma di semicerchio.

- Coloque el segundo relleno en la parte delantera de la cola y déle la forma de un semicírculo.

- View of hair paddings in place.

- Ansicht der angebrachten Haarpolster.

- Vista delle imbottiture per capelli collocate nella corretta posizione.

- Vista de los rellenos de cabello colocados en su sitio

- Divide ponytail into 2 sections. Brush first section and shape firmly over padding. Twist tail and place under padding.

- Pferdeschwanz in 2 Teile aufteilen. Erstes Teil bürsten und fest über das Polster formen. Die Strähne verdrehen und unter das Polster schieben.

- Dividere la coda di cavallo in 2 sezioni. Spazzolare la prima sezione e conferire una forma precisa al di sopra dell'imbottitura. Attorcigliare la coda e collocarla sotto l'imbottitura.

- Divida la cola en 2 partes. Cepille la primera parte y vaya dándole forma encima del relleno. Enrolle el extremo y colóquelo debajo del relleno.

- Hair grip twisted tail at neck

- Verdrehte Strähne am Hals festklemmen.

- Collocare la forcina sulla coda attorcigliata posta sul collo.

- Sujete con horquillas en la nuca el extremo enrollado.

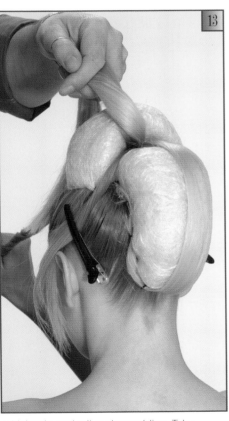

- Hair grip end tail under padding. Take second section of ponytail.

- Ende der Strähne unter dem Polster festklemmen. Zweites Teil des Pferdeschwanzes nehmen.

- Collocare la forcina sulla coda estrema al di sotto dell'imbottitura. Prelevare la seconda sezione di coda di cavallo.

- Sujete con horquillas el extremo de la cola debajo del relleno. Tome la segunda parte de la cola.

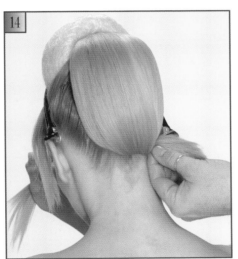

- Repeat process on this side.

- Vorgang auf dieser Seite wiederholen.

- Ripetere l'operazione da questo lato.

- Repita la operación en este lado.

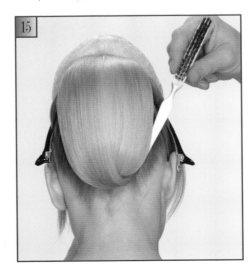

- Leave out a fringe at front and brush back to base of top padding.

- Einen Pony an der Vorderseite lassen und zum Ansatz des oberen Polsters zurück bürsten.

- Lasciare una frangia sulla parte anteriore e spazzolare all'indietro fino alla base dell'imbottitura superiore.

- Saque un flequillo en la parte delantera y cepille el cabello hacia atrás, hacia la base del relleno superior.

17

18

19

- Place hair grips on scalp at base of padding.
- Haarklemmen am Kopf an den Ansatz des Polsters stecken.
- Collocare le forcine sul cuoio capelluto alla base dell'imbottitura.
- Coloque horquillas en el cuero cabelludo, en la base del relleno.

- Wrap right tail (from step 5) around side of padding and over front to cover hair grips.
- Rechte Strähne (von Schritt 5) um die Seite des Polsters und zur Abdeckung der Haarklemmen über die Vorderseite wickeln.
- Avvolgere la coda destra (a partire dalla fase 5) intorno alla parte laterale dell'imbottitura ed al di sopra della parte anteriore per coprire le forcine.
- Envuelva la cola derecha (del paso 5) alrededor del lateral del relleno y por encima de la parte delantera, para tapar las horquillas.

- Hair grip tail on opposite side.
- Strähne an gegenüberliegender Seite festklemmen.
- Collocare la forcina sulla coda che si trova sul lato opposto.
- Sujete con horquillas la cola del lado contrario.

- Repeat same process on left tail.
- Denselben Vorgang mit der linken Strähne wiederholen.
- Ripetere la stessa operazione sulla coda sinistra.
- Repita la misma operación en la cola izquierda.

20

- Divide top hair into 2 sections.
- Obere Haare in zwei Partien aufteilen.
- Dividere i capelli superiori in 2 sezioni.
- Divida el cabello de arriba en 2 partes

- Cover half of padding with right section and cross tails over to left side of padding. Hair grip to hold.
- Die Hälfte des Polsters mit der rechten Partie abdecken und die Strähne über die linke Seite des Polsters kreuzen. Mit Haarklemme befestigen.
- Coprire metà dell'imbottitura con la sezione destra ed incrociare le code verso il lato sinistro dell'imbottitura. Collocare la forcina per assicurare la presa.
- Tape la mitad del relleno con la parte derecha y cruce las colas por encima hacia la parte izquierda del relleno. Sujete con horquillas.

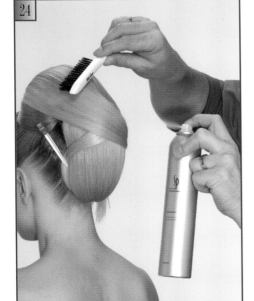

- Repeat process with left section.
- Vorgang mit linker Partie wiederholen.
- Ripetere l'operazione con la sezione sinistra.
- Repita la operación con la parte de la izquierda.

- Hide remaining tails and hair grip to hold.
- Übrige Strähnen verstecken und mit Haarklemmen befestigen.
- Nascondere le rimanenti code e collocare le forcine per assicurare la presa.
- Oculte el resto de los extremos y sujete el cabello con horquillas.

Video 1

"Long Awaited"

Running time approx.
45 minutes

Six long hair designs
from Patrick's European
collection.

Video 2

"Long Awaited 2"

Running time approx.
60 minutes

Six more long hair looks
from Patrick's Royal
collection.

Video 3

"Long Awaited 3"

Running time approx.
45 minutes

Six new styles to give
you that extra edge in
the fashion stakes of
dressing long hair.

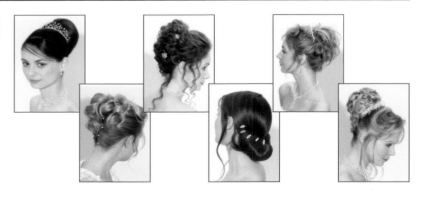

Video 4

"The Bridal Collection:
Part 1"

Running time approx.
45 minutes

Classic long hair techniques
and contemporary
styling create the perfect
bridal video.

Video 5

"The Bridal Collection:
Part 2"

Running time approx.
45 minutes

Six more beautiful step
by step bridal styles.
*Video 4 and 5 are
available as a set on DVD.*

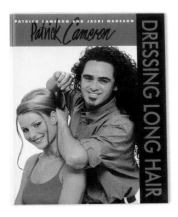

Patrick Cameron: Dressing Long Hair

Patrick's first book is a timeless classic. Featuring over 30 different long hair designs and techniques.

- A magical mix of twists, weaves, curls and braids.
- Over 450 full colour photographs.
- Detailed instructions and professional tips on styling and dressing long hair.

Patrick Cameron: Dressing Long Hair Book 2

- 15 step-by-step long hair styles
- Hundreds of detailed step-by-step photographs.
- Imaginative format of fold out pages to view at a glance

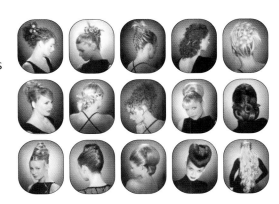

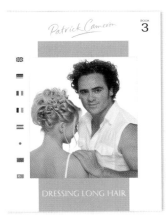

Patrick Cameron: Dressing Long Hair Book 3

- 15 step-by-step long hair styles
- Hundreds of detailed step-by-step photographs.

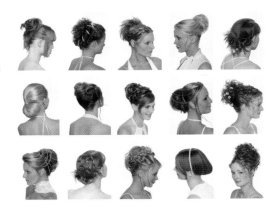

Synthetic hair padding

Long hair styling brush

All merchandise is available from:

Marco Everard

Patrick Cameron Limited

30 Aden Grove

London N16 9NJ

United Kingdom

Tel/Fax: +44 (0) 20 7923 0599

email: **marco@patrick-cameron.com**

www.patrick-cameron.com

Patrick Cameron has justly earned his place in hairdressing's hall of fame as one of the world's leading platform artists, giving him the title, 'The Maestro of Long Hair'.

A regular on television screens both in the UK and overseas and appearing at the most prestigious global hairdressing events all over the world, Patrick continues to educate and inspire many with his visual and often avant garde stage productions. Using his skills gained whilst working as a salon stylist and platform artist, he combines the commercial aspects of speed required for salon work with the theatrical, which enthralls his audiences.

Taking his inspiration from an eclectic variety of sources, Patrick has year after year grabbed the hairdressing headlines when presenting his innovative collections.

In addition to his global appearances and London based Training School, Patrick always takes time out of his busy schedule to visit at least five UK colleges each year where he will present Look and Learn seminars to eager young students, many of whom otherwise would not get the chance to see him demonstrate and present his many talents.

Patrick's philosophy is one that has taken him around the world many times and is one that translates well into any language. "My aim is to create natural looks that make women feel feminine," says Patrick. "When I am presenting on stage I try to break down my techniques into simple step by step instructions so that my audiences can go away and think 'I can do that'. If they leave the show feeling like that, then I have done my job"

Patrick's zest, energy, vitality and dedication to his craft seem never ending. One of the most charming and talented people you could ever meet, Patrick has justly earned his title, 'The Maestro of Long Hair'.

"Breakfast at Tiffany's" 1996

"Tango" 1997

"Opera" 1998

"Global Tribe" 1999

"Arts and Crafts" 2000

"Nightlife" 2001

"Visionaire" 2002

"Bohemian Revolution" 2003

"Provocateur" 2004

"Cream" 2005

In 1997 Patrick Cameron opened his own training school to give students intensive tuition in the art of dressing long hair. Courses take place in London and around the world on a regular basis under Patrick's personal guidance and supervision.

"I like to teach students just one or two steps at a time to break down the style into a logical, easy to understand structure," says Patrick. "Usually we cover at least four styles a day and the results, using this method with small groups of students is superb. My students have ranged from newly qualified hairdressers keen to come to grips with long hair, to experienced professionals looking for further inspiration. The exclusive nature of this course allows me to concentrate on each person's individual needs."

1997 eröffnete Patrick Cameron seine eigene Friseurschule, in der er seinen Studenten und Studentinnen die Frisierkunst an langem Haar zeigt. Die Kurse finden regelmaβig in London und rund um den Globus unter Patricks persönlicher Fuhrung und Aufsicht statt.

„Ich zeige meinen Studenten jeweils nur ein, zwei Schritte, damit sie die logische, leicht verständliche Struktur der Frisur begreifen", so Patrick. „Normalerweise bringen wir unseren Studenten mindestens vier verschiedene Frisuren pro Tag bei. Glauben Sie mir, mit dieser Methode mit kleinen Studiengruppen lassen sich die Ergebnisse wirklich sehen! Zu mir kommen Fiseure, die ihren Abschluss gerade erst in der Tasche haben und wissen mochten, wie sie am besten mit langen Haaren umgehen, aber auch Friseure mit langjähriger Erfahrung, die neue Anregungen suchen. Der Kurs ist so aufgebaut, dass ich mich ganz nach den Wünschen der einzelnen Teilnehmer richten kann."

Nel 1997 Patrick Cameron decise di aprire una scuola dedicata esclusivamente all'arte della acconciatura raccolta. I corsi si tengono a Londra dove Patrick risiede e a volte in trasferta in altri paesi del mondo sempre sotto la guida e supervisione personale di Patrick.

"Mi piace dimostrare agli studenti uno o due passaggi alla volta per spiegare il look in modo logico e facile da comprendere," dice Patrick. "Di solito realizziamo un minimo di quattro stili al giorno, e i risultati quando si ha un numero ridotto di studenti sono straordinari. Fra i partecipanti ci sono sia parrucchieri appena qualificati che desiderano lavorare con i capelli lunghi che professionisti esperti alla ricerca di nuove idee. La natura esclusiva di questo corso mi consente di concentrarmi sulle esigenze di ogni persona."

En 1997, Patrick Cameron abrió su propia escuela para ofrecer a los estudiantes formación intensiva en el arte de peinar el cabello largo. Los cursos tienen lugar en Londres y en otras partes del mundo con regularidad bajo la supervisión y el asesoramiento personal de Patrick.

"Me gusta enseñar a los alumnos uno o dos pasos a la vez, para desglosar el peinado en una estructura lógica y fácil de comprender", explica Patrick. "Normalmente cubrimos como mínimo cuatro peinados al día, y los resultados de utilizar este metódo con grupos reducidos de estudiantes son excelentes. Entre mis alumnos se cuentan desde peluqueros que acaban de obtener el título, ansiosos por aprender a tratar el pelo largo, hasta profesionales expertos que buscan nueva inspiración. La naturaleza exclusiva de este curso me permite concentrarme en las necesidades individuales de cada persona."

For further information on the Patrick Cameron Training School, please vist our website at:

www.patrick-cameron.com

or contact Studio Manager

Marco Everard
Patrick Cameron Limited
30 Aden Grove, London N16 9NJ,
United Kingdom
Tel/Fax: +44 (0) 20 7923 0599
email: marco@patrick-cameron.com

For further information about Patrick Cameron Limited, please contact his business partner:

Sue Callaghan
Patrick Cameron Limited
PO Box 124, Chester,
Cheshire CH1 6ZF United Kingdom
Tel: +44 (0) 1244 880807
Fax: +44 (0) 1244 881140
email: sue@patrick-cameron.com

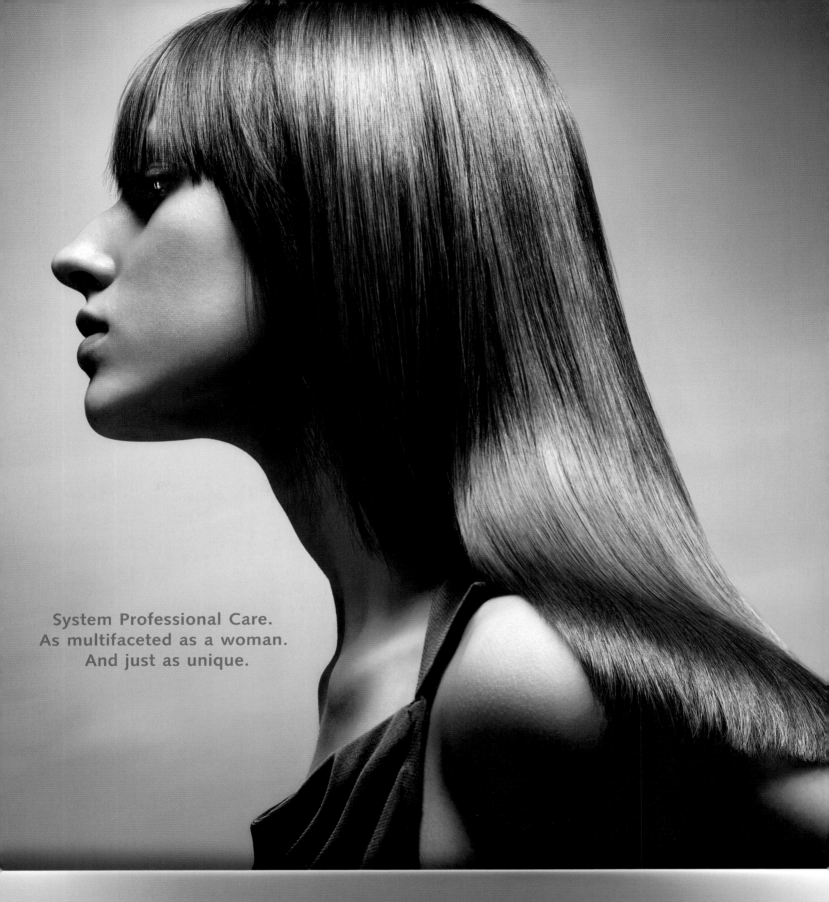

System Professional Care.
As multifaceted as a woman.
And just as unique.

System Professional Care provides customised care for any woman´s hair. The exclusive, multifaceted range can fulfil any care requirement of the hair or scalp. The individually formulated active ingredient combinations provide the best care for all hair types.
System Professional – exclusively from selected salons.

Beautiful hair needs an expert.

Treat your hair to a beauty day.
With System Professional
Keratin Oil and Power Mask.

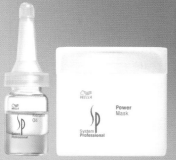

System Professional Keratin Oil and Power Mask:
the caring effect of these two products just couldn´t
be better. Yet together they´re even more effective.
For the combination of an enriched special treatment
and an exclusive two-phase concentrate immediately
provides stressed hair with a wealth of essential
ingredients with an affinity to hair, restructuring it
from within and giving it maximum shine.
System Professional – exclusively from selected salons.

Beautiful hair needs an expert.

Beautiful hair needs an expert.

Hair
PATRICK CAMERON

Photography
Alistair Hughes

Make-up and clothes styling
Alison Chesterton

Hair styling products
Wella

Hair styling equipment
Babyliss Pro

With thanks to
Marco Everard
Sue Callaghan
Alexander Herzberg
Angela Vivado
Fred Dettlev
Helmut Schueler
Paul Jones
Will White
Maureen Barrymore
Phil Ollerenshaw

USA Distributor
Dennis Bernard
142 Ely Harmony Road, Freehold, N.J. 07728
Tel: 732-308-9595
Fax: 732-308-9608
www.DennisBernard.com
email: info@DennisBernard.com

Designed by
Umbrella Communications

First published 2004 by **Patrick Cameron Limited**, 30 Aden Grove, London N16 9NJ, United Kingdom.

ISBN 0-9541106-1-7

Pre-press by Studio Fasoli Verona

Printed by Eurografica Vicenza